The Last of the Free Enterprisers: The Oilmen of Calgary

J. D. HOUSE

"Some day—in the millennium—there may be no need for his type. At present homage is due to it from those who think themselves superior, and who possibly are."

E. M. Forster, *Howards End.*

THE CARLETON LIBRARY NO. 122
Published by Macmillan of Canada, A Canadian Company, in association with the Institute of Canadian Studies, Carleton University

To Marjorie and in Memory of Charles Hunter

Canadian Cataloguing in Publication Data

House, John D., 1944 –
  The last of the free enterprisers

(The Carleton library; no. 122)

Includes bibliographical references.
ISBN 0-7705-1846-x pa.

1. Petroleum industry and trade—Alberta—
Calgary. 2. Executives—Alberta—Calgary. I.
Carleton University. Institute of Canadian
Studies. II. Title. III. Series.

HD 9574.C23A675   338.4'76655'0971   C79-094913-x

29,428

Printed in Canada for
The Macmillan Company of Canada Limited
70 Bond Street, Toronto, Ontario M5B 1X3

Contents

Tables

Figures

Preface

Despite the proliferation of literature on the international oil industry in recent years, very little has been written about oilmen themselves. This book is an initial attempt to fill in that gap. Although much of the material which follows bears upon the political economy of oil and of multinational corporations, I have chosen not to analyse it in those terms in the present work because it would distract me from my main purpose. That purpose is to present a descriptive and interpretive ethnography of the oilmen of Calgary during a specific historical phase, the oil crisis of the mid-1970s. It is a study of oilmen *as* a community, and of oilmen *within* the larger Canadian community. As far as possible, I will allow the data to speak for themselves in presenting a sympathetic understanding of the oilmen's social world, a world that they perceived to be in crisis at the time of my research.

Only in the final chapter, which relates some of the findings to larger questions about international and national petroleum politics and economics, do I intrude my own ideas explicitly into the analysis. In that, I can be seen to be working towards a third position, different from either the oilmen's themselves or their radical critics'. But that position, which advocates a more directly regulated form of capitalist enterprise within the Canadian oil industry, needs to be more fully developed in a subsequent work. My present concern is more strictly ethnographic.

Calgary oilmen feel themselves to be misunderstood and unfairly disliked. In their view, academics and radical politicians oppose them in the name of romantic and ill-conceived forms of nationalism and socialism; provincial and federal governments increasingly impinge upon their freedom and effectiveness for their own short-sighted political ends; and the general public falsely accuses them of massive profiteering at the public's expense.

To these views, the oilmen reply with their own version of reality. They consider themselves to be hard-working, technically competent, and economically efficient in serving Canadians through finding and developing crude petroleum and natural gas, producing it, transporting it, refining it, and marketing petroleum products for the nation's industries, residences, and automobiles. For them, there is no contradiction between public service and private profit-making. The latter both allows the former and is legitimated by it. Government infringement and public disapproval must, therefore, be due to misunderstanding. Industry is at fault only to the extent that it has been guilty of poor public relations; it has failed to get its messages across to the public.

As an attempt at an objective account of the oil industry, and sympathetic understanding of oilmen in the Calgary oil community, this ethnography is in line with the industry's professed aims. Written, however, from an outsider's perspective (and one sympathetic to Canadianization, to improved government control of energy resources, and to many aspects of socialism as preferable to capitalism), it does not make a case for the industry, nor is it written in terms of the industry's own rhetoric. Indeed, one of its aims is to analyse that rhetoric in terms of the oil community's organizing myth, the myth of free enterprise. This is a myth not only in the sense that it distorts economic reality, both present *and* past—it appeals to oilmen mainly as a romanticized, ideal past—but also in the more important sociological sense that it both symbolizes and reinforces the unity of the Calgary oil community. It serves, in Emile Durkheim's sense, a positive function for internal social solidarity.

But, because it distorts reality, and because it has only negative appeal for external critics, the myth of free enterprise has become a barrier to the oil community's attempts to convey its messages. The rhetoric only reinforces what everyone suspects of oilmen anyhow. I believe, however, that oilmen do have something of importance to say to the rest of us, and one of my intentions is to try to convey those messages in different words, words that oilmen themselves may not recognize nor even agree with.

The theme cannot be adequately expressed at this point. In general terms, it is that the malaise that oilmen feel (or at least

felt in the early part of the 1970s) is less economic than com-
munal, their fear is as much for their social and personal
identities as for their material well-being. But their economic
rhetoric prevents them from articulating these more primitive
feelings. The strength of the feelings, I will submit, and the
vigour with which outmoded notions about free enterprise are
upheld, reflect something that is healthy and valuable within
the oil community. Without becoming its advocate, I want to
convey, if not an understanding of, at least a feeling for what
that something is and its implications for the contemporary
Canadian energy scene.

The pursuit of this theme subsumes three interrelated aims
which can be more easily articulated:

1. To analyse the social structure of the Canadian oil industry at the micro level, particularly of its exploration and
   production phases: of the various socioeconomic units
   involved; of their internal organization; and of their in-
   terrelationships.

2. To describe the oilmen of Calgary as a community (a
   group of people with shared interests, aspirations, career
   possibilities, satisfactions, and beliefs and values) and to
   show how oilmen as a community are conditioned by the
   social structure of their industry.

3. To assess the future viability of the Canadian oil community, in particular to ask what lessons outsiders, including critics, might learn from a better acquaintance with its
   operations; and, conversely, to suggest how Calgary oilmen themselves might better adapt their behaviour and
   their rhetoric to the real energy prospects and problems
   facing Canada in the last part part of this century.

I am grateful to the following people for their help in re-
searching oilmen, and in preparing this manuscript: Margaret
Gall, Ann Fietz, Gordon Myers, Larry Deboice, Bill Johnston,
Jon Brehaut, Wayne Rowe, Sandra Doucet, and Vera Edge-
combe. Roger Krohn and my wife, Jeannie, provided helpful
comments on an earlier draft of the manuscript; and the latter
was a source of support and encouragement throughout the
research and writing. Imperial Oil Limited helped immensely
by providing a "no-strings-attached" research grant, and by
allowing me to study their Calgary operations in some detail.
In particular, I would like to thank the many oilmen of Cal-

gary who contributed generously of their time and interest to this research; and the few who have read and criticized parts of the manuscript. If I have not come to agree with the oilmen on many issues, I have come to respect them as a hard-working, well-intentioned breed of people with an enviable sense of community loyalty and solidarity.

THE CARLETON LIBRARY

A series of reprints, original works, and
new collections of source material
relating to Canada, issued under the
editorial supervision of the Institute of
Canadian Studies of Carleton University,
Ottawa.

CHAPTER ONE

Introduction: Calgary and Its Oilmen

Calgary, Alberta, is the oil capital of Canada. Historically, this has been due to chance as much as anything else. It happened that the first significant discoveries of oil and gas in western Canada were in southern Alberta early in this century. Since Calgary was the nearest large town, it developed as the exploration and production headquarters during the Turner Valley phase of the industry from 1914 through the 1930s (Davis, 1969:20–23).

But oil exploration and production did not become big business in Canada until Imperial Oil's major discovery at Leduc, Alberta, in 1947 touched off a "dynamic decade" of major oil discoveries in which Alberta became increasingly industrialized, prosperous, and powerful (Hanson, 1958). Although Leduc is only sixteen miles south of Edmonton (which has become an important service and pipeline centre for the industry), Calgary had already become the administrative centre. New companies, branches, and government offices established themselves there because it was known as the oil capital. During the late 1960s and early 1970s, improved communications and methods of transportation allowed the oil companies to centralize their operations and consolidate Calgary's position. The city is now firmly established as the "Houston of the North", the heart of exploratory activities for the oil industry in Canada. The viability of Calgary's economy and of its oil community depend not only upon prospects and government regulations in Alberta, but also upon those in other provinces, in the federally administered areas in Canada's northern frontier, and in the offshore area of the east coast where jurisdictional rights are currently in dispute between federal and provincial governments. The oilmen of Calgary are now the oilmen of Canada, an essential group in any consideration of the nation's energy prospects.

The contemporary importance of Calgary is indicated in Table 1:1, which shows that 428 of 644 oil companies operating in Canada in 1973 cited it as the location for their head office.[1] These include all the largest independent Canadian companies (such as Dome Petroleum Limited, Home Oil Company Limited, Panarctic Oils Limited), and the Canadian subsidiaries of large foreign companies that confine their Canadian operations to exploration and production (such as Mobil Oil Canada Limited, Chevron Standard Limited, Amoco Canada Petroleum Limited). The large, integrated oil companies (including the four largest—Imperial Oil Limited, Gulf Oil Canada Limited, Shell Canada Limited, and Texaco Canada Limited) all have their head offices in central Canada, mostly in Toronto, near the largest Canadian refining and marketing areas. But each of these also conducts its exploration and production operations from Calgary, under the direction of senior and middle managers who are based locally. As Table 1:1 shows, a number of American oil companies operate branch plants in Canada, although the more usual pattern is for a foreign company to establish a Canadian subsidiary with its head office in Calgary.[2]

TABLE 1:1   Head Office Locations of Oil Companies Operating in Canada

Head Office	Number	Per cent
Calgary	428	66.5
Edmonton	21	3.3
Toronto	30	4.5
Montreal	5	0.9
Other Canadian	58	9.0
Total Canadian	542	84.2
Foreign (mainly U.S.)	102	15.8
TOTAL	644	100.0

SOURCE: Nickle's *Canadian Oil Register, 1972 – 73.*

An obvious implication of these facts is that oil dominates the economic and social life of the city. Some 13,125 people were employed in petroleum-related industries in 1971 (compared to 5,700 in Edmonton).[3] Although this is only 7.38 per cent of the labour force, it represents a well-paid, highly educated, highly visible segment of the population whose members participate as leaders in most of the city's social, cultural, recreational, and political affairs. Oil means wealth, not only in the form of high salaries (Calgary geologists and engineers are among the highest-paid professionals in Canada) but also, more dramatically, in the form of the royalties, rents, and profits that underpin the fortunes of many individuals and families who have struck it rich (and continue to strike it rich) as individual capitalists and entrepreneurs in the oil industry. This money stimulates local businesses of all kinds, and creates local employment (Hanson, 1958: 286 – 89).

On the exploration and production side of the petroleum industry, the way in which the labour force is divided between city and countryside is revealing. Nearly all the manual workers, the direct explorers for and producers of oil and gas, live and work in rural areas—often quite remote areas in northern Alberta, British Columbia, and Saskatchewan, as well as in the Beaufort Sea, the Arctic islands, and the stormy waters off the shores of Nova Scotia, Newfoundland, and Labrador. These men—the technologists on geological and geophysical exploration crews; the roughnecks, roustabouts, and tool pushers on drilling rigs; the workers on oil production sites and in gas processing plants—are *not* the oilmen of Calgary. They are a dispersed and invisible proletariat who make no mark on the urban social scene. Calgary oilmen, by contrast, are more prestigious types: professional workers, managers, and entrepreneurs. Professional workers—the geologists, geophysicists, and engineers responsible for technical analysis and professional recommendations about where petroleum might be found and how it should be produced—are in the majority. These people view themselves as professionals and potential managers rather than workers, and with justification, as most managers are recruited from their ranks. For blue-collar workers, upward mobility is extremely difficult to achieve. The most that they can aspire to is a position as tool pusher on a rig[4] or as field supervisor of production operations.

In the past, geologists, geophysicists, and engineers themselves spent a substantial portion of their time early in their careers "in the field". But field trips have declined in importance, although they continue to play some part in training. This decline is largely the result of the massive impact of the computer revolution upon the oil industry. Geophysicists have become expert interpreters of computerized seismic data, geologists of computerized electrical well-logs, and engineers of computer simulations of producing oil and gas fields. The oilmen of Calgary rarely encounter oil.

This is equally the case for managers and entrepreneurs. Managers administer resources: financial capital, land, physical plant, machinery, exploration and production rights, raw materials, and people. Entrepreneurs make decisions about the uses of those resources. There are many entrepreneurs in the Calgary oil community. They include senior-level managers in large companies who enjoy some degree of decision-making authority in addition to their administrative responsibilities, businessmen in small oil companies or service companies, and independent consultants. Indeed, the continued viability of small business operations that work co-operatively with the major oil companies helps give the Canadian oil industry its unique character.[5]

It is this character, I think, that sets the tone for the social and cultural life of Calgary. It is a businessman's city that rewards hard work, and values material prosperity, economic growth, political conservatism, and community service through voluntary associations. At the same time, it maintains the myth of the frontier, symbolized by the annual Calgary Stampede. Oilmen continue to be genuine explorers of the Canadian frontier, albeit in contemporary and sophisticated ways. Like Calgary itself, they feel that this distinguishes them from those in the metropolitan centres of eastern Canada. This western identity, part myth and part reality, can be better appreciated when seen in the context of the history and the social characteristics of Calgary oilmen.

BACKGROUND AND SOCIAL CHARACTERISTICS OF CALGARY OILMEN

Alberta, like the rest of western Canada, was originally settled as a giant bread-basket for Ontario and Quebec, and as a market for their manufactured goods. This left the hinterland prairie economy extremely vulnerable to both natural and market fluctuations. These combined adversely to create a dire and prolonged depression in Alberta during the 1930s. World War Two brought short-term relief from this, but the end of the war was a mixed blessing as people feared a return to pre-war dependency, vulnerability, and poverty. In view of this previous history, it is not surprising that the Leduc discovery was welcomed euphorically by Albertans. Nor is it surprising that American capital, expertise, and manpower were also welcomed as the only available means of developing the new wealth and opportunities as rapidly as possible. Conditions were favourable, and the combination of vigorous capitalist development under American leadership, sound management of petroleum resources under the Alberta Energy Conservation Board, and the co-operation of the federal government in opening up protected Ontario markets for Alberta crude oil west of the Ottawa Valley succeeded in promoting the rapid growth of Alberta's oil industry. Table 1:2, which summarizes the province's net value of production over the years, illustrates this shift from an agricultural to an agriculture-and-mining-based economy. Note, however, that Alberta continues to depend heavily upon *primary* industry. The failure to progress in manufacturing towards the 1970 Canadian average of 56.4 per cent of net value of commodity production, combined with the fact that oil reserves have begun to decline, helps explain Albertans' distrust of central Canada, and their taking a hard line on maximizing their income from future oil production.

Over the years since Leduc, another less obvious but equally important change has occurred. This is the Canadianization of the Alberta oil industry—Canadianization not of ownership (the industry is still about two-thirds foreign-owned) but of the socially more important element of personnel. As Table 1:3 shows, most oilmen in Calgary today are Canadians, and most of these in turn come from either Alberta or one of its neighbouring provinces.[6] Of the random sample of Calgary oilmen surveyed, 91.4 per cent were Canadian citizens. In addition, many of the Americans who have been in this country for a long time, though they retain their U.S. citizenship, profess a strong allegiance to Canada.

This Canadianization of oil-industry personnel reflects the multinational corporations' strategy of *incorporating* locals into their subsidiaries in developed countries (Tugendhat, 1971: 193; House, 1978); but it has also involved a real transformation of an important sector of the population, and this is our current focus. A quarter of the Calgary oilmen come from farming backgrounds, and another 30 per cent from working-class backgrounds (see Table 1:4). Albertans' allegiance to the

TABLE 1:2 Net Value of Production in Commodity-Producing Industries, Alberta

	1935		1940		1945		1950		1955	
	$(thousands)	%	$(thousands)	%	$(thousands)	%	$(thousands)	%	$(thousands)	%
Agriculture	79,394	53.9	147,781	58.5	212,707	52.8	331,066	44.1	332,403	25.9
Mining	16,096	10.9	27,851	11.0	41,713	10.3	122,543	16.3	303,752	23.7
Electric Power	4,572	3.1	5,810	2.3	8,227	2.0	13,863	1.8	28,858	2.2
Manufacturing	23,769	16.1	37,747	14.9	78,548	19.5	123,893	16.5	263,309	20.5
Construction	21,000	14.3	29,000	11.5	53,000	13.1	147,700	19.7	338,700	26.4
Other	2,514	1.7	4,524	1.8	9,108	2.3	11,280	1.6	15,929	1.3
Total	147,345	100.0	252,713	100.0	403,303	100.0	750,345	100.0	1,282,951	100.0

	1960		1965		1969		1970*		1971*	
	$(thousands)	%	$(thousands)	%	$(thousands)	%	$(thousands)	%	$(thousands)	%
Agriculture	329,278	21.4	511,904	23.0	566,702	17.5	563,000	16.3	603,000	16.0
Mining	349,115	22.7	690,524	31.0	1,103,604	34.3	1,293,000	37.3	1,486,000	39.3
Electric Power	48,587	3.2	69,389	3.1	94,460	2.9	108,000	3.1	118,000	3.1
Manufacturing	339,377	22.1	475,343	21.4	702,820	21.7	693,000	20.0	735,000	19.5
Construction	445,551	29.0	470,816	21.1	753,132	23.3	796,000	23.0	824,000	21.8
Other	24,008	1.6	9,346	0.4	10,082	0.3	11,000	0.3	11,000	0.3
Total	1,545,915	100.0	2,227,321	100.0	3,235,800	100.0	3,464,000	100.0	3,777,000	100.0

*Estimates

SOURCE: Reprinted with permission from *Industry and Resources, 1973*, Alberta Bureau of Statistics.

TABLE 1:3   Distribution by Place Raised (random sample of 349
Calgary entrepreneurial, managerial, and professional
oilmen, 1974)

PLACE	NUMBER			%
Canada	276			79.08
Western Canada	243		69.63	
British Columbia	17	4.87		
Alberta	135	38.68		
Saskatchewan	66	18.91		
Manitoba	25	7.16		
Ontario	21		6.02	
Quebec	4		1.15	
Atlantic Provinces	8		2.29	
United States	27			7.74
Great Britain	15			4.30
Other European	20			5.70
Other	11			3.15
TOTAL	349			100.07

TABLE 1:4   Fathers' Occupations of Random Sample of Calgary
Oilmen, 1974 (per cent)

Professional	18.0
Management-Administration	8.3
Small Business	8.6
Clerical	9.1
Skilled Trades	14.3
Unskilled	12.0
Farmer	24.0
Salesman	5.1
Other	0.6
	100.0

N = 348

oil industry is based partly upon economic self-interest, partly upon the genuine pride of the local people in their ability to succeed in the national and, increasingly, the international petroleum scene. The following career account is typical of many contemporary Albertans' personal biographies.[7]

> I was born in Lethbridge, raised in Medicine Hat and Calgary. My dad was in the life-insurance business. I guess I had my mind made up that I was going to be a petroleum engineer when I was fifteen years old. This was the year when the Leduc discovery was being made. This was soon followed by Redwater. There was an awful lot of excitement and talk about the money to be made. It all sounded very logical to me, an industry that it would be a good idea to get into on the ground floor. I worked with Imperial for one summer before I graduated and got to know a little about the organization and its people, and I looked at some of the alternate offers from other major companies and I guess by the process of elimination I ended up with Imperial. I've stayed with them for twenty years. I've spent a year in Tulsa with the old Carter Research Laboratory there, and then I've been on various assignments here and there. I've just come from four months at the Humble lab in Houston.

This process of career selection whereby a number of Albertans have become oilmen appears, from the individual's perspective, to be a matter of free choice and equal opportunity. But other information suggests a rather different process. Calgary oilmen are incredibly homogeneous in their social characteristics. In the first place, as the term "oilmen" implies, they are nearly all male—99.1 per cent of our sample.[8] Women's liberation has a long way to go in the Calgary oil community, where virtually all the professionals and managers are male, and all the secretaries are female. This latter group constitutes the urban proletariat of the oil industry, in that its members totally lack any sense of working-class solidarity, organization, or consciousness. Even the few women who are accepted as geologists, geophysicists, and engineers experience difficulties. They have to play down their femininity in their work roles to prove that they are as much "oilmen" as anybody else, and they face innumerable difficulties in their attempts at career mobility.

> The girls in the department don't want to have a female supervisor. If you want to get along, you can't just start ordering people

around. I'm kind of limited here because I think the company has a policy that you can't send a woman out into the field. You lack a lot of basic understanding because you can't get out into the field. Basically, just being a woman is a disadvantage.

The oilmen in our sample were homogeneous in many other ways as well. They are nearly all married,[9] support the Progressive Conservative party in federal and provincial politics, express preferences for established religions,[10] and derive from British or northern-European ethnic stock.[11] To put it negatively, the oilmen of Calgary include almost no women, no radicals, no Jews, no native Indians, no Inuit, no East Indians, no blacks, and no French Canadians. This is not because Calgary oilmen are unusually sexist and racist, but rather that the complex processes whereby people choose and are chosen for careers in the oil industry favour some groups and discriminate against others. Once such a homogeneous community becomes established, it tends to perpetuate itself. Change could only come from a conscious effort from within or without the oil community to create new, special-status opportunities for women and members of minority groups in Alberta and the rest of Canada.

It seems unlikely, however, that such an impetus will come from oilmen themselves in the foreseeable future, partly because their social homogeneity reinforces their community cohesion and ease of sociability. This, in turn, strengthens the informal ties and processes through which business is conducted on a day-to-day basis within the Calgary oil industry.

CHAPTER TWO

Corporations and Entrepreneurs

No doubt because of the visibility of their local gas stations and the focus of the media, a few major oil companies are viewed by the public as monolithically dominating the industry in Canada. There is some truth in this, but it distorts and oversimplifies a more complex reality. The Canadian oil industry is actually organized as a complicated network of hundreds of companies of varying sizes and types. To understand the industry, we need to analyse the nature and role of each of these types; but first the industry as a whole needs to be located within the larger system of which it is a part—that is, contemporary international capitalism.

The world capitalist system can conveniently be thought of as divided into metropolitan and hinterland regions (Frank, 1967). The metropoles are both economically and politically powerful. They are the major decision-making centres, are heavily industrialized, and provide most of their citizens with a high material standard of living. The hinterlands are economically and politically weak and dependent, their degree of industrialization is low, and their populations suffer from chronic underemployment and poverty. They provide both raw materials for the metropoles and markets for the latter's manufactured goods. Furthermore, their capital-intensive, natural-resource and manufacturing industries are largely owned and controlled by foreign corporations with headquarters in the metropoles which appropriate the hinterland's economic surplus, thereby reinforcing and perpetuating the inequality and dependency of the metropolis-hinterland relationship.

Canada's position within this system is not clear cut. On the one hand, its major resource and manufacturing industries are owned and controlled by foreign capital (Safarian, 1966; Government of Canada, 1972), mainly by multinational corporations with head offices in the United States, which has become the dominant metropolitan power during this century. On the other hand, Canada is highly industrialized and a large proportion of its population enjoys a high material standard of living. Canada is best viewed, I would suggest, as a *privileged hinterland* region within the world capitalist system, as a kind of favoured adjunct of the United States. Canada's resources have been developed as a natural northern extension of American expansion. Canada's population, unlike those of Third World countries, has been integrated into this expansion and has ridden to prosperity on the coat-tails of American capitalism. The costs of this prosperity have been some erosion of sovereignty, an increasing annual drain of economic surplus, and perpetual dependency (Levitt, 1970); but, again unlike Third World countries, Canada has enjoyed a privileged dependency in an almost benign patron-client relationship.

The growth of the Canadian oil industry clearly reflects this pattern. Before the Leduc discovery, the centres of the industry were in southern Ontario and Montreal, where imported petroleum was refined to provide Canadian markets. The major cities, particularly Montreal and Toronto, were satellite centres in the world capitalist system which, in turn, developed their own metropolitan-hinterland domination over western Canada. The major discoveries of oil and natural gas in Alberta during the late 1940s and throughout the 1950s occurred within the context of these established ties between Canada as hinterland and the United States as metropole, and between western Canada as hinterland and central Canada as metropole. Calgary, as the satellite centre for Canadian petroleum exploration and production, has found itself involved in two different sets of metropolis-hinterland ties.

Integrated Canadian subsidiaries continue to have their head offices in central Canada, so that the exploration and production departments in Calgary report to and are controlled by head offices in Toronto (Imperial, Shell, Gulf) and Montreal (BP Canada, Petrofina Canada, Texaco Canada). These in turn are ultimately controlled by their parent corporations in New York, Pittsburgh, London, and Belgium. Canadian subsidiaries involved only in exploration and production, on the other hand, have their head offices in Calgary, and the Calgary office reports directly to the parent company in New York, Chicago, Dallas, or Houston. More recently, some Canadian subsidiaries operating out of Calgary have reversed the historical trend by diversifying into refining and marketing, mainly in western Canada and the northwestern United States. (For example, Pacific Petroleums Limited, Total Petroleum [North America] Limited, and Union Oil Company of Canada Limited). These ties are illustrated in Figure 2:1.

This metropolis-hinterland perspective locates the Calgary oil industry within a larger system; but it gives a rather one-sided, mechanical view that fails to do justice to the energy, dynamics, and independent emergent properties of its local operations. We have already seen that the industry in Calgary

FIGURE 2:1 Metropolis – Hinterland Ties of the Canadian Oil Industry

is staffed largely by Canadians. These personnel should not, for the most part, be viewed simply as administrative pawns of their central-Canadian head offices or foreign parent corporations. Rather, they are active participants in decision-making processes, both as technical experts and as manager-entrepreneurs.[1] Furthermore, many of them are employed not by foreign subsidiaries, but by large privately and publicly owned Canadian independents, or a host of small local oil companies, or a myriad of local service-and-supply companies. Still others work as independent consultants. To appreciate better the dynamics of the oil industry in Calgary, we need to examine each type of unit that comprises it, and to try to grasp the principles of organization whereby the units are interrelated in their day-to-day operations.

THE CANADIAN MAJORS

The dominant units of the Canadian oil industry are the subsidiaries of large, multinational oil companies. The term "major" was originally used to refer to seven such companies (five American, one Dutch/British, and one British) that once exercised a virtual monopoly of the industry outside of North America and the communist world. These were: Exxon Corporation (originally the Standard Oil of New Jersey); Mobil Corporation (originally the Standard Oil of New York); Standard Oil Company of California (trade name Chevron); Gulf Oil Corporation; Texaco Incorporated; the Royal Dutch/Shell group of companies; and the British Petroleum Company Limited (Odell, 1970: 13–15). More recently, these have been joined by a number of other oil companies that have developed into large multinationals. These include the established American "independents" (such as Occidental Petroleum Corporation, Superior Oil Corporation, Continental Oil Company, and the Standard Oil Company [Indiana]); and a group of European companies with varying degrees of state ownership (such as Société Nationale de Pétroles d'Aquitaine [Aquitaine], the Compagnie Française Pétrole [CFP], Petrofina [of Belgium], and the Italian state company, Ente Nazionale Idrocarburi [ENI]).

In discussing the contemporary oil scene in Canada, I will use the term "major" to refer to *all* of the above types of companies. But it is striking that the six largest oil companies in Canada are subsidiaries of six of the original "seven sisters". Of those, only Standard of California fails to have a subsidiary in the list of Canada's largest fifty companies (*Canadian Business*, July 1976: 38).

Imperial Oil, which is 69.5 per cent owned by Exxon Corporation, is by far the largest oil company in Canada, with gross assets in 1975 of $4.1 billion and 15,321 employees, making it twice as big as its nearest rival, the third largest Canadian company by sales, and the second largest by net income.[2] Shell Canada (79 per cent owned by the Royal Dutch/Shell group) and Gulf Oil Canada (63.9 per cent owned by Gulf Oil Corporation) vie for position as the second and third largest companies with 1975 sales of nearly $2 billion each. Texaco Canada (68.2 per cent owned by Texaco Incorporated) and BP Canada (65.6 per cent owned by the British Petroleum Company Limited) are also large integrated companies, ranking fourth and fifth in size in Canada. Texaco used to display both patterns of metropolis-hinterland control, as Texaco Exploration Canada Limited, a wholly owned subsidiary, operated out of its Calgary head office in exploration and production; the two Texaco companies have recently merged their operations in the same pattern as the other majors. (*Financial Post*, February 25, 1978: 26).

The integrated Canadian majors built up their strength largely by buying out independent Canadian companies, with the original owners maintaining some equity interest. Subsidiaries confining their operations to exploration and production tend to be wholly owned with tighter control from head office. Canada's two largest resource companies, Mobil Oil Canada Limited and Amoco Canada Petroleum Company (*Financial Post* 300/Summer 1976), are wholly owned subsidiaries of Mobil Oil Corporation and Standard Oil of Indiana. Other important integrated Canadian majors include Petrofina Canada, Sun Oil, Pacific Petroleums, and Total Petroleum (NA); while Hudson's Bay Oil and Gas (53.1 per cent owned by Continental Oil Company, 21.2 per cent by the Hudson's Bay Company), Canadian Superior Oil Limited, Aquitaine Company of Canada, Union Oil Company of Canada, and Atlantic Richfield Canada Limited (recently bought by the national oil company, Petro-Canada) are Canadian majors confined mainly to exploration and production.

THE LARGE INDEPENDENTS

The Canadian oil industry is dominated by foreign ownership. In addition to the Canadian majors, a number of American independents—smaller U.S. companies which have extended their continental operations north of the border—also have subsidiary offices in Calgary. Among the largest are Ashland Oil Canada Limited and Murphy Oil Company, but there are numerous other companies. A few other companies are best described as bi-national. The most important is Canada's seventh largest oil company, the fully integrated Husky Oil. Its head office is in Calgary; until a share purchase by Alberta Gas Trunkline Limited in 1978, the largest shareholder was a Denver family who were formerly Canadian; most of its exploration and production is in Canada; and most of its refining and marketing is in the United States.

To qualify as "mature", a petroleum company must be fairly large, and must have sufficient production to finance a signficant proportion of its operating and exploration costs from internally generated funds. (This notion of corporate "maturity" will be discussed more extensively in Chapter Four.) By these criteria, very few oil companies have been able to attain and maintain maturity while preserving majority Canadian ownership. The main reason for this is that a successful Canadian company represents a tempting plum for aggressive foreign competitors. It provides petroleum resources, local manpower and knowledge, and access to internal markets in Canada. Exxon, Shell, Gulf, Texaco, and numerous others initially established or consolidated their operations in Canada by buying out local independents. It was simply "good business". And Canadian companies have been willing to sell, not only to make a lot of money, but also to gain access to the financial resources, technology, and expertise that the multinational affiliation provides. Even the two most notable contemporary exceptions, Dome Petroleum Limited and Home Oil Company, have barely survived as independent Canadians. Dome is currently 45.2 per cent foreign owned, and may find itself under pressure if its extremely expensive exploration program in the Beaufort Sea proves unprofitable. Dome is important, however, for showing that a Canadian company *can* participate and compete successfully in the big leagues of petroleum exploration. Home Oil would have sold out recently, but was prevented by the Canadian government and was salvaged for Canada by the Consumers' Gas Company's buying 49.7 per cent of its outstanding shares. The only other large, successful Canadian petroleum companies have had massive financial backing from other sources within the country unrelated to petroleum. Pan-Canadian Petroleum Limited is 87 per cent owned by Canadian Pacific Investments Limited, while Panarctic Oils Limited is a consortium of Canadian independents involved in arctic exploration with the backing and 45 per cent ownership of the federal government. More recently, the federal government has established a national petroleum company, Petro-Canada; and the provinces of Alberta, British Columbia, and Saskatchewan have all set up provincial companies. Whatever its merits and demerits, it is clear that "free enterprise" in the Canadian oil industry has meant foreign ownership. There are, however, numerous small Canadian companies operating out of Calgary as well, and a few of these may be able to break into the ranks of mature independents in the not too distant future.

THE SMALL INDEPENDENTS

The North American petroleum industry is unique in its happy juxtaposition of large corporate and small entrepreneurial enterprise. This is owing largely to the land-tenure systems which allow interested parties to acquire oil and gas exploration rights and permits (from individuals in the U.S., from governments in Canada) with only small outlays of initial capital. As there is more exploration to be done than even the majors can undertake, there is always room for the "little guy" who hopes to strike it rich by finding oil. Much of the colour and verve of the Calgary oil community comes from this sector of its population. Its members eschew becoming organization men in large corporate bureaucracies; indeed, to compete for manpower, the large oil companies themselves have had to institute greater flexibility and openness in their internal organizations than might otherwise have been the case.

Today, the small oil companies survive as the scavengers of the industry. Unable to compete with the majors and large independents for prime prospects, particularly in expensive frontier exploration, they operate on the fringes—re-evaluating prospects that the majors have examined and abandoned, drilling on the outskirts of established fields, or, most romantically, drilling wild-cat wells in unexplored areas considered as poor prospects on the basis of seismic information. In 1972, independents accounted for 82 per cent of western Canada's wild-cat drilling.[3] Most of these efforts fail, and there is a high turnover rate of small oil companies. A few succeed, and either go on to become established independents or, more usually, sell out to larger companies. The matter of scale is important in understanding the viability of these small companies. An exploration play may be so small that it promises to add little to the nation's reserves and is not worth the majors' efforts— they have bigger and more ambitious projects for their massive but still limited resources. As oilmen put it, the majors are only interested in "elephant hunting", but success in finding small game, "rabbit hunting", can mean personal fortunes for individual entrepreneurs. Most of Calgary's oil millionaires, apart from a few lucky families who happened to enjoy freehold rights to mineral exploration in the early part of this century,[4] have made their money and continue to make their money in this way—this is an ongoing, viable form of contemporary entrepreneurial activity.

Small oil companies, by contrast with large ones, are much more firmly stamped by the personalities of their owners and leaders. The company is the tool of the entrepreneur, designed and manipulated by him to make himself and (if he forms a public company) his shareholders rich. Ownership and control are almost evenly divided between the two dominant types of partner, capitalists and entrepreneurs. Capitalists provide money. Entrepreneurs mobilize resources and provide technical and managerial skills. The first initiative may come from the entrepreneur who looks for people to invest in his company, or from a group of people with money to invest who seek out a Calgary oilman with an established reputation for setting up companies and conducting exploration plays. One important source of exploration capital in western Canada has been "drilling funds" from wealthy Americans. The U.S. government has allowed its citizens, even in other countries, to deduct the full amount of money invested in oil and gas exploration from taxable income. This has been a tremendous incentive for those in high-income-tax brackets. If oil is found, they strike it rich; if not, they can at least deduct the full amount of their investment for income-tax purposes.

Many small Canadian oil companies have been heavily dependent upon that source of financing and have been careful to nourish contacts south of the border.

> We have some internal money, and then we have external money; we have what you would call investors, people in the high-income bracket in the States that invest in oil and then they can deduct their intangibles from their gross incomes which lowers their income. If they make a million dollars a year, then they have to pay taxes on say, $600,000. So if they put half a million dollars in oil exploration, they can deduct that half a million from their gross income, so their net income is only $500,000; and they only have to pay taxes on say $300,000. So the government is in a sense putting in 50¢, and they're putting in 50¢. They're 50¢ dollars. We have probably 60 or 70 per cent of our money coming from people like this.

Recently, as drilling incentives have improved within the U.S., and as the American government has planned to bar foreign exploration from its allowable deductions, the Canadian government has responded by making similar opportunities available for wealthy Canadians to become even wealthier, while protecting small oil companies (and thereby Canadian exploration) from crippling capital shortages.

This dependency upon a limited external source of financing distinguishes the small companies from the established majors and independents. Some one- or two-man firms choose to remain private, at least initially. This gives them complete control over their operations and, if they do happen to make a viable discovery, the profits are all theirs. Often, once they have established production, they will use their reserves as a selling point to go public, and use the capital raised by selling shares to finance further exploration and to develop their production. Unsuccessful private companies can tide themselves over in lean periods by accepting consulting contracts and making deals for others on a contract basis. Most companies do aim to grow to the extent that they will be able to finance operations and expansion largely from current cash flow. This means finding and developing sufficient petroleum reserves that they can rely upon a continual and secure income from their own petroleum production. Some Canadian companies (e.g., Siebens Oil and Gas, Ranger Oil) appear to be reaching this point. Particularly if their North Sea discoveries prove profitable, they may soon be classifiable as mature Canadian independents. Another growth strategy, one less often practised because of greater attendant risks, is to sell off productive properties once they are developed. This provides more funding for increased exploration in the short term, but leaves the company extremely vulnerable should exploration prove unsuccessful.

In the pages that follow, we will have more to say about small oil companies, about their relations among themselves and with their larger and more powerful competitors, and about the careers of their members and the rewards their jobs provide. First, however, we need to fill out our introductory sketch of the units that make up the social organization of the Alberta oil industry.

DRILLING COMPANIES

Oil companies, large and small, are the entrepreneurs of petroleum exploration and production, in that they mobilize and make decisions about the use of resources—where to conduct geological and seismic exploration, where and when to drill for oil, and how that oil should be produced and transported to refineries. But oil companies as such do surprisingly little of the physical work that such operations require. Over the years, they have gradually come to contract out more and more work to specialist firms. The most important of these are the drilling companies, and the drilling industry itself is now international in scope and dominated by its own multinationals.

As of 1974, the Canadian Association of Drilling Contractors listed fifty-two drilling-contractor members, and another thirty-two service-rig members. While the large international drilling companies have recently focused their expertise and activities upon the larger-scale, more technically challenging, and more lucrative offshore drilling scene, conventional onshore drilling in Canada is now dominated by Canadian-owned companies with head offices in Calgary. The oilwell-drilling industry is now about 90 per cent Canadian owned.[5] This trend away from foreign ownership is illustrated by Brinkerhoff Drilling

Canada Limited. Formerly owned by the large private American firm, Brinkerhoff Drilling Incorporated, it was bought in 1972 by a Toronto-based company, Upper Canada Resources. This type of affiliation with larger industrial organizations, which provides a kind of corporate family shelter both from the short-term seasonal fluctuations that characterize Canadian drilling and from longer-term market uncertainties, is common. Westburne Drilling Limited, Canada's largest drilling contractor, is a subsidiary of Westburne International Industries Limited; and Sedco Drilling is a division of Bow Valley Industries Limited. Others, such as the large Peter Bawden Drilling Services Limited, and the smaller Garnett Drilling, are independent companies in their own right. A few American internationals, such as Santa Fe International Corporation, have established small subsidiaries in Canada; but, since most offshore drilling to date has been in international waters beyond national government control, the international drilling companies have not experienced the same need as the oil companies to set up Canadian subsidiaries.

The Canadian drilling industry is beset by seasonal fluctuations, exposure to market uncertainties, continual conflicts between management and labour and resultant high worker turnover rates, and structured dependency upon the oil companies. The peak months for drilling in Canada are during the winter, from October through March, when the muskeg of the northern prairie provinces and the icy waters of the Beaufort Sea and Mackenzie Delta are frozen solid. The number of employees of a small, seven-rig drilling company (the largest companies have up to thirty or more rigs) fluctuates from around 45 to about 130 employees during a year. These include a permanent nucleus of managers and staff in Calgary, and the supervisory staff of the company's various field operations. Most workers— the roughnecks (labourers) and other "derrickmen"—are laid off at the end of the drilling season. There is no more work for them to do, and the company cannot afford to keep them on its payroll. This, however, creates perennial problems of labour turnover, and the company tries to employ its best people on a year-round basis.

One man per rig, the tool pusher, is on a permanent basis. But we have the supervisor submit a list of his key people, and we try to keep anywhere from two to three people per rig employed for twelve months—like during the spring break-up when the rigs are inactive they can do a lot of maintenance and repair work, painting, cleaning up, and anything else that we can find them, because we feel that as long as we can keep these fellows around then when we get ready to start out in the Fall their loyalty to us will be greater and they will stick with us.

The drilling business (as well as the service-and-supply and consulting businesses) is vulnerable to market or politically determined slow-downs. In the adjustment period in the early 1970s, when provincial and federal governments responded to high world prices for oil by dramatically increasing royalty and tax takes, oil companies retaliated by slowing down their exploration programs markedly, particularly in Saskatchewan and British Columbia. This meant fewer drilling contracts and economic hardships for many drilling companies, some of which adapted by moving rigs south of the border where the U.S. government was encouraging renewed exploration efforts.

SERVICE-AND-SUPPLY COMPANIES

The oil companies' policy of contracting out most of their work has created business opportunities for hundreds of smaller firms that provide a myriad of services and supplies dazzling in their range and diversity. These can include: core operations like geophysical exploration and interpretation, rig repair and maintenance, the provision of specialized chemical fluids for drilling (called "mud"), and the construction of gas-processing plants and oil-production facilities, as well as such peripheral but essential items as helicopter services, catering, and "scouting" for information. Some companies specialize in designing and manufacturing particular types of equipment. The following technical description conveys the kind of complexity involved.

We specialize in drilling recorders that record the various drilling functions: rotary speed (how fast the bit is turning), pipe weight, pump pressure, the fluid pressure that washes the cuttings out of the well, and how fast their pumps are stroking, and things like this. We have one item that got us started in business, called a deviation tool. In drilling in the plains here, they will try to keep it as straight as possible to steer toward a target area. We just have a small tool that measures this drift.

Many of the companies that specialize in such equipment are subsidiaries of American and other foreign firms. Indeed, some are essentially local distributors of foreign manufacturers. More mundane products and services are supplied by local Canadian companies.

The success of service-and-supply companies depends upon their establishing and maintaining business and personal contacts with key people in the oil companies. Theirs is very much a selling operation, as they attempt to establish good reputations for their products and themselves. This is particularly the case for one type of service, information exchange. Information, particularly geological and geophysical information, is a key resource in the oil industry, since it is essential for making rational decisions about new drilling prospects. Large oil companies operate their own scouting departments, but smaller companies must depend upon specialist service companies which act as middleman brokers of information. They gather data both from official sources in governments and industry associations, and from personal contacts throughout the industry. As one man put it: "We spend a great deal of time maintaining contacts with people in 90 per cent of the industry." This information is then provided to clients on a fee-for-service basis, the charges being either for particular pieces of information or, more usually, for weekly reports supplied at a regular monthly fee. Most oil companies provide such information fairly freely to the brokers because the system works on a reciprocal basis.

> Our job is to collect the information and get it out to the industry as fast as possible. Some people do not really want to release information but do so because it is a co-operative venture. You scratch my back and I'll scratch yours.

By using a broker, the company requesting information is able to maintain its anonymity, and majors sometimes work through brokers for this purpose; but the main reason for using a specialist seems to be convenience and economy, as the larger companies also engage in directly reciprocal information exchanges.

As we shall see, establishing and maintaining personal contacts is even more crucial for consultants.

CONSULTANTS

Many small Calgary companies (they number in the hundreds) refer to themselves as "consultants". Most of them are one- or two-man operations, but they range in size up to companies with as many as seventy or eighty members expert in various aspects of oil and gas exploration and production. They differ from the small independents in that they do not attempt to find oil for themselves and, consequently, do not depend upon raising capital; and from most types of service companies in that what they have to sell is a specialized expertise directly related to the finding and producing of petroleum. Consultants are of many varieties, but we can distinguish three main types.

The first type, the "technical expert", most clearly resembles consultants in other fields. He sells specialized knowledge and advice in return for a fee, and may be held on a retainer basis by a number of companies that want to maintain access to his services as needed. Experts representing a wide variety of areas — from corrosion engineering, to computer-simulation techniques, to petroleum-accounting systems — are to be found in this group.

The second type of consultant is the "independent professional". He is a geologist, geophysicist, or engineer who, having had training and experience in one or more large oil companies, decides to go out on his own and work for various companies on a contract basis. This provides greater freedom and independence and the chance to make more money if things go well. But it is risky, as contracts are hard to come by in slow periods. The independent professional differs from the technical expert in that he offers routine exploration and production skills, rather than a highly specialized expertise. Probably the most common type is the geologist who lives by contracting to "sit on wells" for his client companies. This involves going into the field to drilling sites to oversee the work of the drilling contractor on behalf of the client, and to collect and initially examine rock specimens as they are removed from the drill hole. Small companies like to hire such independent professionals on a contract basis, as it is cheaper than keeping them on permanent staff. When their own geologists are busy, either because of a peak in exploration activity or because they are involved in some more technically demanding work at head office, large companies also hire independent professionals from time to time. Because of their vulnerability to market swings, and the difficulties many have of drumming up business on a regular basis, independent professionals often work on a sub-contract basis with large consulting firms. This provides greater security, as the firms find them jobs, but it represents an admission of partial failure as they in turn must limit their cherished independence by agreeing to refer all their business through the firm.

The third type of consultant (I will call him "the deal-maker") is the most interesting. The deal-maker is like the small independent in that his livelihood depends upon his entrepreneurial skills. The difference is that, whereas the small independent puts together deals for his own company, the deal-maker does it for other people in return for a fee, a commission, or a percentage interest in the venture. Deals include the putting together of exploration plays, the purchasing of producing properties, and the organization of corporate acquisitions and mergers.

I've been talking to a mining company that would like to get involved in the oil and gas industry. They have large amounts of capital behind them so they can take on almost any size of deal that I can put to them. By and large they are still being a little bit cautious about the industry, so they want to buy producing reserves or a company that has producing reserves. They are not quite ready to go and explore on their own to any extent. Once they get some cash flow then they would certainly go and explore. I have another couple of clients, well, they would look at a million-dollar deal but that's getting a little small for them; they would prefer to look at a deal that would run from probably $3 or $4 million up to $15 or $20 million. There's another company that I work for, but it's very small and they are looking for marginal deals, perhaps up to half a million dollars. Then there's an associate of mine in the States who's a sort of tax-dollar raiser. So I'll put a deal to him—here's a piece of property that involves some production and some development drilling. To interest him it has got to involve drilling because that's where the tax dollars are. In his situation, it could be any size deal. If it was a $20 million deal, it would take a little longer. He would simply get on the plane and go to New York and start hitting his contacts over there, and maybe in a big deal he would have to bring a lot of other people in with him, New York financial people. So, the $20-million deal for him would have to be slightly better than for the Canadian mining company to take care of all these guys in between.

These deal-makers, and consultants generally, are highly dependent upon maintaining good business contacts within the oil community. In particular those they sustain relations with include: characters known as "deal-sniffers", who have reputations for coming up with good ideas about potential deals even though they might not organize them themselves; bankers who know of deals that might be attractive because some client is in financial trouble; and lawyers who have clients in legal trouble. The deal-makers and small independents (often the same entrepreneurs at different stages in their careers) show clearly that, despite oilmen's fears about the future, free enterprise is currently alive and well and thriving in Calgary.

In practice, a single person or firm often becomes involved in each of the three types of consulting we have considered. This is particularly so for large consulting companies.

We're a one-stop shop. We do everything, well, except for geophysics. But we have our own drilling-production section, which can handle anything from drilling to production operations. We were project manager on a big exploration play recently; we ran the whole show—ordering materials, negotiating contracts, and that sort of thing. We have a reservoir engineering group which does everything from highly sophisticated, three-dimensional, three-phased numeric simulation to evaluations, underwritings, mergers, arbitrations, the whole bit within the reservoir group. We have our own gas-plant-design people who design and supervise the construction of gas plants; we're just putting the finishing touches on a $25 million plant at the moment. We even have our own rural gasification group and pipeline group.

The importance for the flexibility and adaptability of the oil industry of having consultants of such variety and scope available is a theme that will be developed in Chapter Three.

ASSOCIATIONS AND REGULATORY AGENCIES

Inconsistently, oilmen do not really believe in "free enterprise" in the literal meaning of the term. It is more nearly correct to state that they believe in private enterprise regulated so as to

favour the interests of the industry itself. Regulation is necessary to avoid the social anarchy that a truly free-enterprise,
free-market system would entail (Polanyi, 1957; Bliss, 1974) —
anarchy in the form of cut-throat competition, uncontrolled
market fluctuations, speculative stock-market booms and busts,
and wasteful uses of resources. Oilmen also manage to refrain
from complaining about such government measures as tax exemptions and exploration incentives that "interfere with" the
free-market system for their benefit! Except for the very early
Turner Valley days, the Canadian oil industry has always been
highly regulated, and this has been one of its strengths. The
current concern of the industry is not with regulation as such,
but with what it considers to be over-regulation and, particularly, regulation that appears contrary to its members' economic interests.

In part, the industry regulates itself through its two national
associations, the Canadian Petroleum Association and the Independent Petroleum Association of Canada. But most regulation is imposed by federal and provincial governments and
their public services. Broad policies are established by the federal and provincial legislatures, while day-to-day operations are
governed by the National Energy Board and various provincial
boards, the most important being the Alberta Energy Conservation Board.

The existence of two trade associations reflects the diverging
and sometimes conflicting interests of multinational and locally
based oil companies. The Canadian Petroleum Association
(CPA) was established during the Turner Valley days to represent the interests of all oil companies in Canada. But, after
Leduc, it came to be dominated by the majors. The independents wanted to open up eastern-Canadian markets by having
the Interprovincial Pipeline built to Montreal, but the majors
were supplying their eastern refineries with cheap crude oil
from Venezuela and the Middle East, and preferred to "bank"
the more expensive Albertan crude in the ground for future
use. This policy hurt the independents, as they needed the cash
flow from Canadian production as soon as possible and
wanted immediate access to the Montreal market. They formed
their own organization, The Independent Petroleum Association of Canada (IPAC), to promote this aim. In the event, the
federal government sided with the majors and eastern-Cana-

dian consumers who wanted cheap energy, and the pipeline was terminated at Sarnia in 1953. The recent oil crisis has shown this decision to be short-sighted, as foreign exporters have drastically increased the price of their crude, and eastern Canada's security of supply has been threatened by the Arab oil embargo.

As of 1973, the CPA had 235 member companies, 100 of them active petroleum explorers and producers. It had a permanent staff of seventeen, most stationed at Calgary headquarters, but worked mainly through forty standing committees that could call on some 800 to 900 experts from the member companies. The CPA continues to be dominated by the majors, and the large annual fee effectively precludes most small independents from joining. Large independents belong to both trade associations.

IPAC had 216 member companies in 1973, including 153 independent explorers and producers. (In addition, there are a number of Associate members, mainly companies and financial institutions that provide services of various kinds to the industry.) Since the opening up of the U.S. market to Canadian crude in the late 1960s and the extension of the Interprovincial Pipeline to Montreal during 1975, the interests of IPAC and the CPA have converged. They often combine their efforts, both on the various technical committees and in joint submissions to governments on energy policy and regulations. The majors endorse the continued existence of the Canadian-dominated IPAC for political and public-relations reasons. As the president of one wholly owned subsidiary put it: "We feel that it's to our advantage to have the Independent Petroleum Association, with its heavy Canadian involvement, represent the interests of our industry." This reflects a changing role for the associations in recent years. They continue to promote internal co-ordination and joint research and technical discussions among member companies, and to make technical submissions to governments; but more and more their top officers have taken on a spokesman role for the industry, advocating its interests both to governments and to the general public. The CPA in particular has become the public voice of the industry.

Of the many government bodies that regulate the oil industry, the most important for day-to-day operations in Calgary is the Alberta Energy Resources Conservation Board (AERCB).

The board was originally set up in 1938 to regulate production in Turner Valley, and Alberta was fortunate to have it in place to regulate the rapid growth of the industry during the 1950s.

Effectively, the board's function has been to guard against the excesses and ravages of a truly free-enterprise system of petroleum exploitation—like those that characterized the growth of the industry in Texas and Oklahoma (O'Connor, 1955) and the early years in Alberta. Ironically, it was called into being when the majors tried but failed to impose rationalized pricing and production rates upon small independents anxious to make a fast buck. Through its centralized planning, the board has, rather unwittingly, helped consolidate the economic dominance of the majors and large independents.

The term "conservation" refers to the board's efforts to maximize the amount of petroleum that can ultimately be produced from an oil and gas reservoir. It regulates the spacing of wells and the rates at which operating companies are allowed to pump up the oil and gas. If too many holes were drilled, and if the reserves were depleted too quickly, pressure levels within the reservoir would be reduced and less oil and gas could be recovered. To promote conservation in this sense, the board insists that the many companies that may be involved as successful explorers in adjacent drilling leases "unitize" their activities to put a new field on production. Through unitization, the company with the largest interest, invariably a major or large independent, becomes the "operator" of the field. Each of the participating companies is given a share of production revenues depending upon its interest in the field, and the operator receives an additional operating fee. Large companies thereby control small companies' production and, until recently, the majors were also able to set crude-oil prices through their control of pipelines and refineries. Prices are now fixed by governments.

The AERCB also rationalizes the industry (interferes with free enterprise) through a system of "prorationing", which attempts to bring anticipated demand into line with anticipated supply. Where unregulated supply would exceed expected demand and thereby lead to destructive price-cutting, each producing field is limited to producing a certain quota based mainly upon its percentage of potential supply. Prorationing was of crucial importance during the rapid expansion of the supplies during the

1950s, became less so as the opening of the U.S. market allowed for maximum exploitation during the 1960s (not necessarily to Canada's benefit), and has become important again in the mid-seventies as exports are being phased out by federal government decree.

Oilmen themselves, including the small entrepreneurs, recognize the board's legitimacy and its contribution to their own long-term interests, despite its curbing of free enterprise. Table 2:1 shows the favourable response of Calgary oilmen when asked to rate the board's performance. The board receives a much more favourable rating than either federal or provincial governments. Board members work closely with the industry and, indeed, many of them are former oilmen. There is no doubt that the AERCB and similar boards in Saskatchewan and British Columbia have played major roles in the growth of Canada's oil industry. As energy becomes a national priority, and as exploration and production grow in the northern and offshore frontiers, this regulatory responsibility will shift more and more to the National Energy Board in Ottawa.

TABLE 2:1   Ratings of Performances of Alberta Energy Resources Conservation Board, Provincial Government, and Federal Government by Random Sample of Calgary Oilmen (Percentages—N = 348)

	VERY POOR	POOR	FAIR	GOOD	VERY GOOD
AERCB	1.2	4.6	15.0	40.3	38.9
Provincial government	14.1	28.2	39.2	16.1	2.3
Federal government	48.6	39.4	10.3	1.1	0.6

CONCLUSION

Calgary is, and promises to continue to be, the administrative centre for oil and gas exploration and production in Canada. The growth of the industry has occurred within a global and national context of metropolitan-hinterland ties, between the United States and Canada on the one hand, and central Canada and its western hinterland on the other. This wider perspective helps explain both the role of foreign capital in developing Alberta's energy resources and the continual insistence of the federal government over the years upon its "right" to regulate that development's impact upon Ontario and

Quebec. Too great a focus upon this perspective, however, would give an overly determined view of the Alberta industry. It has its own dynamic, one which in recent years has come to challenge metropolitan control. And it has its own characteristic organizational weaknesses and strengths. It can be conceived, loosely, as a socioeconomic system comprising units, relationships among the units, and principles of organization. This chapter has described the main units: Canadian majors, large independents, small independents, drilling companies, service-and-supply companies, consultants, and trade associations and regulatory agencies. But how do these units fit together as a dynamic system?

CHAPTER THREE

How the Industry Works

In trying to understand how the exploration and production phases of the Canadian oil business work, I will analyse the industry in terms of a number of principles of social organization that appear to give a kind of tentative order or logic to its everyday operations—that is, that make it into a socioeconomic system.[1] "Principles of social organization" are neither universally necessary laws nor mechanical cause-and-effect sequences, but something more tentative and transitory than either. Social systems have histories—they emerge, persist for some time, change for both internal and external reasons, and characteristically pass into oblivion or at least are so dramatically altered that they are best thought of as new types of systems. I want to emphasize here the dual nature of social systems. On the one hand, once they emerge, once they are "in their prime", they do take on an apparent life of their own. They develop their own logic, their own principles of organization to which their members must adapt. They do not determine behaviour mechanically, but they do severely constrain people's choices and career possibilities. In this sense, as sociologists are wont to claim, individual and group behaviour is structured by the larger system.[2] On the other hand, the members of social systems (in our case individual oilmen, companies, associations, regulatory agencies) are adaptive, active, sometimes aggressive participants. They can and do occasionally challenge the workings of the system in minor or even major ways. In other words, there is a *dialectical* relationship between social systems and their members, and this dialectic makes them historical.[3]

In this chapter, as in the preceding and subsequent ones, the focus is on one side of this dialectic, on the Canadian oil industry during its prime in the 1970s. What makes the industry tick? What are the rules that govern its organization? How do its various parts fit together into a kind of patterned system? This is our present focus—upon its persistence. But even during the seventies there were changes and, as oilmen began to think of the industry as being in a state of crisis, warnings of still greater changes to come. I want to assess this "crisis" later. But first, what is the system that was felt to be in crisis? What are its principles of operation?

THE DOMINANT POSITION OF THE MAJORS

One purpose of Chapter Two was to dispel the myth that the Canadian oil industry consists solely of a few huge, multinational oil companies that directly participate in all phases of the business. But a counter-myth, that the industry comprises numerous firms of equal status competing on an equal basis, would be even more misleading. The majors (and, secondarily, the large independents) dominate the industry. They do this first because they are by far the largest explorers, producers, transporters, refiners, and marketers of petroleum. Tables 3:1 and 3:2 summarize the situation for 1973 for production (in barrels per day) and exploration (as indicated by net land holdings). The largest company, Imperial, accounted for 17.45 per cent of production, the top five (all majors) for nearly half, the top ten (including nine majors and one large independent) for two-thirds, and the top twenty (including sixteen majors

TABLE 3:1 Production of Crude Oil by Company Rank, 1973

COMPANY RANK (BY PRODUCTION)	AVERAGE BARRELS PER DAY	PER CENT TOTAL PRODUCTION	CUMULATIVE PER CENT
1	262,000	17.45	17.45
2 – 3	265,000	17.65	35.10
4 – 5	196,572	13.09	48.19
6 – 10	276,912	18.44	66.63
11 – 15	177,951	11.85	78.48
16 – 20	131,698	8.77	87.25
21 – 25	72,832	4.85	92.10
26 – 50	101,064	6.73	98.83
51 – 100	16,819	1.12	99.95
101 – 122	846	0.05	100.00
	1,501,694		

SOURCE: Nickle's *Canadian Oil Register, 1973 – 74.*

TABLE 3:2   Exploration (Net Land Holdings) by Company Rank, 1973

COMPANY RANK (BY NET LAND)	NUMBER OF ACRES	PER CENT OF LAND HELD	CUMULATIVE PER CENT
1	71,299,647	9.20	9.20
2 – 3	119,532,286	15.43	24.63
4 – 5	95,618,748	12.34	36.97
6 – 10	134,684,759	17.39	54.36
11 – 15	95,688,700	12.35	66.71
16 – 20	58,098,785	7.50	74.21
21 – 25	41,443,800	5.35	79.56
26 – 35	52,133,977	6.73	86.29
36 – 50	49,577,630	6.40	92.69
51 – 100	43,380,426	5.60	98.29
101 – 286	13,246,523	1.71	100.00
	774,650,743		

SOURCE: Nickle's *Canadian Oil Register, 1973 – 74.*

and four large independents) for nearly 90 per cent. The rest was produced by over 100 small companies. Ten of the largest companies (including seven majors and three independents) held over half of the net land rights to oil and gas exploration; while 186 small companies shared less than 2 per cent of the total. Furthermore, share of production correlates highly with share of net land holdings ($\ell = 0.75$).

These data, computed from the *Canadian Oil Register* which relies upon company-supplied information, may be somewhat inaccurate; in addition, they will change slightly from year to year. Nevertheless, they clearly indicate the dominant position of the largest companies. For 1975 production, *Oilweek* magazine reported that ten companies accounted for 65.6 per cent of total liquids production, and twenty companies for almost 87 per cent as well as nearly 77 per cent of gross natural gas output (May 17, 1976:10). As Table 3:3 shows, the majors are also by far the largest employers, with the big three (Imperial, Gulf, and Shell) accounting for over half of the industry's employees. Again, the correlation between this figure and that for size by production ($\ell = 0.73$) is high. The figure includes refinery and marketing people throughout Canada, but even in Calgary at least half of the industry's employees (52.4 per cent of our sample) work for majors. Despite the large number of

TABLE 3:3   Employees in Canada by Company Rank, 1973

RANK (BY EMPLOYEES)	NUMBER OF EMPLOYEES	PER CENT OF EMPLOYEES	CUMULATIVE PER CENT
1	15,549	25.46	25.46
2 – 3	16,945	27.74	53.20
4 – 5	5,906	9.67	62.87
6 – 10	7,621	12.48	75.35
11 – 25	9,448	15.47	90.82
26 – 50	3,567	5.84	96.66
51 – 100	1,302	2.13	98.79
101 – 298	737	1.21	100.00
	61,076		

SOURCE: Nickle's *Canadian Oil Register, 1973 – 74.*

small independents, most oilmen work for the larger companies. Only 18.2 per cent of the sample worked for companies
with fewer than 100 employees.[4]

Sheer size is the most obvious way in which the major oil
companies dominate the industry. But they also dominate it
organizationally in two ways. The first has to do with business
strategy and decision-making. Indeed, the very existence of
viable independent drilling companies and service companies
in such operations as seismic exploration and geophysical data-
processing has depended heavily upon the majors' withdrawal
from active participation in these areas. In the same way, the
viability of small explorers derives from the big companies'
penchant for "elephant hunting". In a sense, the majors allow
the small companies to survive. Or rather, they have learned to
accept them and use them to achieve a sort of economy of
means in their own operations, rather than drive them out of
business, which would be both economically expensive and
politically unpopular.

In part, the majors also accept the independents because
they can control them through their superior bargaining power.
This is the second way in which the majors dominate the
industry's organization. All other units in the system (and, we
might add, governments and the public as consumers) depend
upon the majors in some way or other. Small companies need
them to help finance their expensive exploration plays and the
development of production; and drilling, service-and-supply,
and consulting companies need them for the work contracts

they provide both directly and indirectly (by making it possible for the small independents to survive). Although the majors also depend in a variety of ways upon these other companies, their bargaining power is much stronger, since the numerous smaller companies are in competition with one another for the lucrative contracts offered by the big companies. In addition, the majors could, if necessary, do the jobs themselves rather than contract them out. In other words, over the years a symbiotic inequality has emerged in the relationships between majors and other kinds of companies. This has become an organizing principle in its own right, and calls for more detailed analysis.

SYMBIOTIC INEQUALITY

Contrary to the earlier predictions of many Marxist and liberal critics, dominance of the economy by large corporations has not meant the destruction of other forms of capitalist enterprise. During the twentieth century, a new balance seems to have established itself between the corporate and the individual forms of capitalist organization. Internationally, the original majors continue to dominate the oil industry, but their share of world markets has decreased since World War Two (Tugendhat and Hamilton, 1975:146–55). A similar pattern has emerged in Canada, where small companies have always maintained a viable presence in the industry, and the market share of Imperial in particular has declined somewhat since the Leduc discovery. The demand for petroleum has been too high, exploration potential too great, and the costs of entry into the industry too low,[5] to allow the majors to consolidate a monopoly position. Instead, they have accommodated to reality by establishing a dominant-partner position.

The majors maintain their position through their vastly greater resources. In Canada, they have more money, better access to outside sources of capital, more skilled manpower, better equipment, and better access to technology than do the independents. And this advantage in Canadian terms is immeasurably strengthened by their international connections. Their extensive primary resources have, in turn, helped them to become major controllers of intermediary resources—resources that are also important for acquiring the ultimate resource—that is, profits (House, 1974). The key intermediate resource in oil exploration is land. In each of Canada's frontier areas in turn, Canadian governments have stimulated exploration interest by making land (exploration rights) easily available to the oil companies. More than others, the majors could afford to take advantage of this policy during the early years of western-Canadian exploration, and they continue to control most of the best prospects there. Their future dominance is guaranteed as well by their acquisition of large amounts of land in the northern frontier regions and off the east coast. (Dome and Panarctic also have large land holdings in the Arctic islands.)

The majors' superior land holdings in Alberta give them a good deal of power, particularly over the small independents. A small company with some capital may find a good prospect and want to begin drilling. As often as not, however, the exploration permit for the area is owned by a major, probably one that has been inactive in that area for years. The small company must then approach the major to try to make a deal; this is called "farming-in" to the permit-owning company's acreage. The major is in an enviable bargaining position. It has no immediate need to make a deal, and may wish to "sit on" the property until higher petroleum prices improve its drilling prospects. Having nothing to lose, it can drive a hard bargain with the small independent. It might agree to a farm-out only on the condition that it be given a guaranteed royalty and a large proportion, perhaps 50 per cent, of the eventual revenue production. The small company must arrange the financing, bear most of the costs, accept most of the risks, and organize the operation. Naturally, small companies tend to resent this.

> Little companies like mine obviously can't carry a large land inventory and we have to work up a play and then try and get the land and get it drilled. Well, in almost every case you find the land is held by a major oil company which is quite comfortable; the rental payments don't bother them and they are exacting some pretty high prices. It's almost standard that they want a 15 per cent gross overriding royalty up until payout and then after the well has paid out they want 50 per cent of the working interest in the well. That irritates me because it's entirely an unproductive burden. You are really paying for nothing, he just happens to be on the land, he's not contributing to the drilling of the well or the discovery of

reserves or anything else. He's just simply a land speculator, that's all he is. That's what I object to, that and the fact that they can hold it up for years, they might not even talk to you, they might not want to farm it out at all. Imperial Oil always used to say that a barrel of oil that you produce is a barrel of oil that we don't produce, so we're not very interested in farming anything out to you that we think has any merit.

(This president of a small independent went on to admit: "I think that if I was Imperial I'd take the same attitude.")

There is, nevertheless, a kind of reciprocity, albeit imbalanced, in this relationship. The majors do agree to farm-outs, and they do refrain from competing too strenuously for the "small-game" prospects. Without meaning too, majors help the independents in other ways as well. They provide access to information and technology and, in particular, they are the main source of small companies' manpower. The majors are the training centres for the industry. They continually lose good people to smaller companies who offer high salaries and more varied work opportunities. They resent this, but are unable to prevent it.

The majors also enjoy benefits from having viable small companies in the industry. Economically, they profit by having their more marginal prospects developed by somebody else with little risk or cost to themselves. But they also benefit politically and ideologically. The existence of numerous companies gives the appearance of free enterprise to the industry as a whole, and gives the lie to critics' claims about monopolization. This strengthens the case for competition that the industry habitually puts to both government and legal review bodies and that its efforts at public relations in general try to promote. Ideologically, the persistence of small independents is thought by oilmen to offer living proof of the merits of the competitive free-enterprise system, and is useful not only for dealing with outsiders but also for helping oilmen reconcile their personal beliefs with their everyday experience. Majors like to think that they are no different "really" from small companies. They are merely bigger.

Relations between the majors and the service companies (including drilling companies and consultants) are more clearly reciprocal.[6] As their name suggests, the latter provide services to the oil companies in return for payments. This is done on a contract basis, and what is striking about the attendant transactions is their formal, businesslike nature, quite unlike the easy informality that characterizes deals among oil companies.[7] Formality and impersonality, even between company representatives who know each other personally, are imposed by the majors despite the service companies' preference for more friendly business relations. The majors' purpose is to enhance competition among the service companies; this, in turn, keeps prices low. The majors have no need for relations with their suppliers beyond the strictly economic. Non-economic comitments could compromise their interest in finding the best service or supply at the lowest price. Their policy is explicitly to "spread the business around". This policy helps keep many small companies viable, and thereby ensures the competitiveness of the oil industry's support sector. The majors, with a nearly monopolistic position as buyers of services, adopt policies that prevent their suppliers from achieving monopolistic or oligopolistic market power as sellers.[8]

A corollary to this policy of spreading the business around is the policy of awarding contracts by calling for tenders on a strictly competitive basis. Oil companies keep lists of potential suppliers who will be contacted when a tender is being called for. New companies can have their names added. A company may be excluded if it has a bad reputation, particularly if it has performed poorly for the same oil company in the past, but this would be unusual. Sometimes the oil companies will request preliminary proposals and preliminary quotes informally; these are usually followed by a more formal call for tenders. The bids received are then judged on their merits. The main consideration is price, but other factors in, say, a contract for drilling an expensive well in the Arctic would include types of equipment, technical expertise, and availability of manpower. Oil executives are adamant that "personal connections" are of only peripheral importance in the awarding of such contracts. Service-company personnel agree, although as the weaker, less secure partner, service companies would prefer to be able to build up guaranteed business through personal contacts.

> Unfortunately, the cost criterion comes in. It seems (and you can put this remark down!) that every now and then you can come up with a good working relationship with a company. Unfortunately,

there is a tendency, perhaps through the accounting profession, to muck a good deal like this up. Maybe an auditor will come up from the States and say: "Is there no other contractor in the country beside this particular company?" For their own internal reasons they have to spread the work around, but I don't think that's the best way to do business. Most service companies prefer to work for independents, as their local managers make the decisions and can give greater weight to factors, including personal contact, other than price. Given the price we'll work for those independents.

Again, the system works to the mutual benefit of the parties, but the major oil companies do maintain the upper hand. They receive good services at reasonable prices, and are assured that these are available to them as needed.[9] The service companies are able to do business that would not be possible were the majors to do the work themselves. One driller commented explicitly on the ingredient of self-interest in this largesse.

We're allowed to exist because the oil companies made the decision to allow contractors to exist. It was based fundamentally on the old game that they figured we'd work for less of a rate of return than they would. The oil companies figure that if we want more, then they'll take us over.

The smaller service companies profit by the majors' policy of sharing the business. Within the terms of most contracts, the service companies are also spared much of the risk-taking. This can be illustrated by drilling contracts. These are of two basic types: footage and day work. The former is a type of piece-rate contract in which the driller is paid by the foot no matter how long it takes to drill the well or what difficulties may be encountered. It is fairly common in areas where drilling conditions are well-known. Day work is paid for at a daily rate, so that the oil companies take the risk that something might go wrong. They are usually asked (and are usually willing) to do this in unknown areas like the Arctic.

In a wider sense, however, the service companies bear more risks than the majors. They are the vulnerable "front line" of the industry when it is besieged by market slowdowns and political uncertainties. At such times, oil companies protect themselves—and hurt their partners—by contracting for less work. Individual consultants are particularly vulnerable to such cutbacks. The central staffs of the larger service companies usually keep their jobs, but their manual workers in the field do not.

THE IMPERATIVES OF COMPETITION

To economists, who define competition as a market system in which no one seller or buyer is large enough to affect price through its own behaviour, the Canadian oil industry is not competitive. In the past, the price of crude oil was set by the majors with one of them, usually Imperial, acting as price leader. They set prices according to a complicated formula based upon the price of Gulf of Mexico oil when delivered to Chicago and including a small discount to make Canadian oil competitive in American markets. Pricing was probably not openly collusive, but the majors implicitly agreed to refrain from price-cutting which could lead to destructive price wars. These were administered prices that took market factors into account, not pure market prices in the economists' sense. Recently, following the lead of the OPEC countries,[10] the Canadian government has taken over the pricing of crude oil in Canada; but this has brought about chiefly a shift in the administration of pricing rather than the radical change perceived by some oilmen.

Economists' refusal to award the term "competitive" to the oil industry has been very influential in shaping popular views of it. In a wider sociological sense, however, the industry *is* highly competitive. Competition, and the *spirit* of competition that it engenders, are central both to the way the industry works and to the way oilmen experience it. Competition as a positive value is a difficult concept to grasp, particularly for critics conditioned to think of it as an "unnatural" human state artificially created by capitalism itself. Yet other interpretations are possible, and it is essential to suspend judgment if one wants to gain a sympathetic understanding of oilmen and their industry.

Critics and apologists show remarkable unanimity in agreeing that the driving forces behind capitalist enterprise are profit-making and growth. These are complementary; profits finance growth, and growth ensures greater profits in the long run. Oilmen themselves would agree. They explain and justify their everyday policy decisions and behaviour as being in the best interests of their shareholders. This is presented as the final tribunal for assessing any decision or action.

As proximate causes of behaviour, the profit and growth motives are no doubt fundamental. All oil companies want to make profits, and most (with some notable exceptions that value smallness for its own sake) want to expand. Nevertheless, such explanations fail to locate these motives within their so-cial-structural context. By analogy with professional sports, the oil business can be seen as a sort of game in which a number of teams (companies) are divided into various leagues (majors, small independents, drilling companies, service companies, consultants). All these teams compete with one another to try to win the game. The winner is the team that scores the most goals, that is, establishes the best land position, finds and produces the most oil and gas, sells it for the highest profits, and achieves the highest growth rates. Fame and glory (status and prestige within the industry) go to the winning teams in each division. But capturing the Stanley Cup is not the only measure of success. You can still have a good season even if you lose out in the play-offs, particularly if you have improved your position in the standings. And, for a major leaguer, it is something just to maintain your first-division status. To extend the analogy to include European soccer, relegation to a lower division means failure. But even for the failures, "there is always next year". Furthermore (here the analogy breaks down), in a "healthy", expansive industry, every team can gain absolutely if not relatively by improving its position over last season. This depends in part upon favourable playing condi-tions, including political support and incentives.

As professional players, oilmen expect and receive rewards based on how much they have contributed to the team's suc-cess. They agree on the legitimacy of this, although there are disputes about what a player is worth, and about who should play on the power play or be appointed team captain. Al-though there is by no means only one big scorer, most would agree on who are the "real oil finders", the top executives, and the best deal-makers. The players also recognize the legitimacy of "trades", of moving to new teams and competing as stren-uously as ever against their former team-mates. Of course the club owners, who put up the initial capital and organized the teams in the first place, are thought to deserve a share in their successes through "a fair return on their investment".

What I want to stress, in drawing this analogy, is that the profit and growth motives are derived imperatives of this competition. We could equally well posit a land-position motive, an exploration motive, a production motive. What compels behaviour is not so much these individual motives as the whole competitive process in which oil companies and their members are implicated by the social organization of the industry. In considering the particular forms of competition, I will focus upon the oil companies, primarily the majors.

In attempting to win the oil-industry game, companies compete for the scarce resources that are the necessary means to that end. The degree and fierceness of this competition vary with the phase of development the industry has reached in any particular territory. The first phase, when the all-important land positions are being staked out, is the most competitive. This is not a pure zero-sum game, as all companies can acquire some land; but it is close to it in that every exploration concession won by your competitors is one that is lost to you. And there is a finite number of good prospects. The game is regulated by government agencies which call for concealed bids for oil- and gas-exploration permits on specified tracts of land. Majors are in powerful positions because they have more money with which to bid, but even they have limited budgets. Furthermore, they have to compete with each other. The trick is to decide upon how much to bid, but this depends upon the exploration potential of the acreage, which is an unknown. Companies compete to glean as much information about it as possible. Initial seismic surveys and geological interpretations give general indications of what the acreage might contain, but the well-logs and successes or failures of wells drilled on adjacent land give a much clearer picture. The operating companies of these wells try to keep such information secret. Their competitors respond by a form of industrial espionage universally accepted in the oil world and known as "scouting". Oil scouts are men employed on either a full-time or a contract basis to find out what other companies have been doing and learning, particularly from their latest drilling programs. They gather such information from all sorts of sources, both reputable and disreputable: official records, private information-exchange companies, informal contacts in the other companies, persuasion (even bribing) of drilling personnel, and spying in person in the field. The last is the most "romantic" form of scouting. The scout conceals himself some distance from a drilling site, fixes his binoculars upon the rig, and attempts to discover whether it is an oil well, a gas well, or a dry hole, and to pick up whatever other information he can about the operation. The rig operator may respond by making life as difficult as possible for the scout (for example, by blocking roads to the site) and by employing various "counter-espionage" techniques designed to disguise what has actually been found in the well. Scouting exploits in the early days are an important part of the folklore of the Alberta oil industry.

> There were lots of funny situations. I can remember up at Rainbow Lake, we hired an Indian to bring some supplies in by horses, because it was in the middle of nowhere. A few days went by and there was no sign of either the Indian or the horses, so we sent up one of the fellows in a plane to try to spot him. He found him and dropped a note down telling him how to get to our seismic crew. We didn't want anyone else to know where it was. But what we didn't realize was that the Indian couldn't read, so he took the note down the road to a competitor's seismic crew. So that blew that one!

Later, when oil developments enter the production phase, competition lessens. Other important resources—manpower, technological information, capital—do not produce the same competitive struggle. For the most part, the majors recruit their new manpower from outside the industry, mainly from university graduates in engineering and geology, and train them themselves.

As we have seen, they do have to compete with smaller companies to try to retain their best people; but this is a fairly benign competition in which the majors have resigned themselves to a certain turnover that has to be replaced annually. And they refrain from compounding the problem by raiding each other. Most inter-company moves are from larger to smaller companies, as oilmen see little point in shifting from one major to another.

Capital is another resource in chronic short supply, particularly for smaller companies, but they do not compete directly with one another for it. The competition is mediated through financial institutions that decide which companies are good financial risks. The majors all have such vast assets that they have little problem in raising loans, and do not need to compete with one another.

Technology is an important resource, and companies try to maintain short-term competitive edges through technological leads (Schumpeter, 1951). In recent years, however, the oil industry seems to have decided that technological information should be made available fairly readily to everyone. As with prices, oilmen agree that the "pooling" of technological know-how is in the best long-term interests of all competitors; short-term "technology wars" could disrupt long-term smooth operations.[11]

After land and information related to bidding for land, the major oil companies compete most strenuously for markets, particularly for markets for their refined petroleum products, which have to be sold to industrial, commercial, and household consumers. In Canada, marketing is a separate phase of the industry, is conducted mainly in central Canada, and is beyond the scope of the present study. Producing companies have little need to compete for markets for their crude oil and natural gas. The majors enjoy assured sales to their own refineries, demand for the product is high, buyers (major companies' refineries and natural gas utilities) are too sophisticated to be influenced by advertising gimmicks, and price and supply quotas are regulated by national and provincial energy boards.

Apart from the race for land, then, competition within the exploration and production phases of the Canadian oil industry is fairly benign. Oilmen also find it *enjoyable*. I have suggested that if one wished to characterize what makes the industry tick the best label would be "the spirit of competition". At the company level, this includes the desire for both profits and growth. If you want to succeed in the oil game, you have got to show a profit and you have got to grow in order to keep up with the competition. At the individual level, this same spirit of competition translates into the need to make a good living and to achieve career success.

But, for the oilman, there is more to competition even than this. It is part of his faith. The competitive system, he believes, imposes a *discipline* upon its member companies that benefits everybody, not only oilmen but society at large. He claims three main benefits: finding petroleum reserves, improving technology, and operating efficiently. More petroleum is found because one company's failure in or rejection of a certain exploration play poses a challenge to another company. Oilmen delight in relating how Bauff Oil discovered Rainbow Lake when Imperial concluded that it contained no crude oil; Bow Valley Exploration discovered Pembina after the majors had rejected it; Eastcan found oil and gas off Labrador after Amoco had given up on its east-coast offshore play. If there had been only one company (e.g., a national oil company), perhaps none of these discoveries would have been made.

Competition also provides the incentive for the development of new technology, both as a means of reducing costs and for gaining short-term advantages over rival companies. Canadian oilmen claim that such incentives are lacking in the Soviet Union, and this explains its striking dependency upon Western technology.[12] Competition also imposes cost efficiencies, as reduced costs mean higher profits and business success. By contrast, oilmen claim, government public services and state-run enterprises know no such constraints and the "waste of the taxpayers' dollars" through sheer inefficiency is subsequently appalling. They shudder at the prospect of having their industry operated on such terms: "Can you imagine what would happen if Air Canada or CN were to take over the oil industry?"

The imperative of competition, then, is a basic organizational principle of the Canadian oil industry. It is institutionalized, it structures behaviour, it is a source of satisfaction, and it is an article of faith. But it is complemented by an equally important principle of co-operation among the units of the system.

THE BENEFITS OF CO-OPERATION

I have already mentioned in passing three ways in which oil companies co-ordinate their activities that involve what could be called "implicit co-operation". The majors implicitly agree to avoid price wars, disruptive technological break-throughs, and manpower raids. These agreements are not the result of overt collusion,[13] but rather of the individual companies' rational calculation of their own best, long-term interests. Suppose you represent the interests of one of ten majors, and that it is thought that one of the companies (nobody knows which one) is likely to make a technological break-through that could severely disrupt everyone else's business. The odds are nine to one that the break-through would be made by one of your major competitors. (The majors have too much respect for each other to have any illusions about these odds.) The best way to protect your long-term interest is to agree to share the discovery should you make it. Major companies seem to have evolved this type of tacit agreement in the process of accommodating each other over the years. Such agreements also favour the interests of the independents, who are kept in the technological know. An example is Imperial's three "lead rigs" which it employs itself to test out new procedures on difficult frontier drilling problems. It passes on successful new techniques to the drilling companies, which in turn use them when working for other oil-company clients, Imperial's large and small competitors. In the short term, Imperial gains a technological lead and also ensures that all the drilling companies that it might need can learn the new technique; in the long term, Imperial gains access to technological advances made by other companies.

The Canadian oil industry is also striking for its *explicit* cooperation in advancing technology and solving common problems. Both the CPA and IPAC have numerous technical committees, and these call upon experts in the member companies. The companies operating in the Mackenzie Delta and Arctic islands have also formed the Arctic Petroleum Operators Association; those off the east coast, the Eastcoast Petroleum Operators Association. Its major committees, such as the environmental and socioeconomic committees, second people from the participating companies who work together to solve common problems. This system is efficient because it both pools the talents of numerous experts and avoids unnecessary duplication of effort.[14]

Information sharing takes many other forms as well. Indeed, it is all but rampant in the industry. In addition to IPAC, the CPA, and various professional associations such as the Association of Professional Engineers of Alberta, government departments of energy and the conservation boards are storehouses of information; and regulations require that, to minimize duplication of effort, all seismic and well-log data be publicly available after a certain time, usually one year. I have mentioned that some service companies specialize in the exchange of information. About a dozen of these information brokers in Calgary deal in geophysical seismic data. Not only do they act as distribution centres for a generalized type of information (Sahlins, 1965), but they also negotiate deals between specific companies where the buyer wishes to remain anonymous. Majors contract out their own seismic programs, but they will sell data to smaller companies through the brokers. Usually, because it has tax advantages, they prefer to build up "credits" with these brokers rather than accept payment in money. These are held in their account by the broker until they can cash them in to acquire some initial geophysical data on a new area in which they have become interested.

The majors and large independents also trade seismic data directly. If, for example, Petro-Canada is interested in some acreage that runs into a block leased by Chevron, it will ask for so many miles of seismic data covering the block, and offer a similar package of data in return. Usually, after some bargaining back and forth, a deal will be negotiated. Although each side hopes to better the other in the deal, the principle governing the exchange seems to be that of a "balanced reciprocity" (Sahlins, 1965) such that, particularly in the long term, each side will fare equally well. Similar trades may be negotiated for well-log information.

Such exchanges save time, money, and effort for all parties, and reduce the level of duplication of effort for the industry as a whole. Again, as in the cases of oligopolistic pricing and technological access, each firm protects its own best interests in the long run, as well as the smooth working of the industry as a whole, through sharing information. This extensive co-operation reflects a mature industry and relatively open resource, as each participating company feels that it can continue to expand even as its competitors do. The pie (Canadian exploration and production potential) keeps getting bigger. The interests of the industry as a whole are furthered in the faith that, to paraphrase a well-known aphorism, what's best for the industry is best for Imperial or Shell or Gulf, or even Numac. One oilman suggested that the capital-intensive nature of the industry frees its employees to participate in technical training programs and industry seminars and meetings, thereby promoting this free flow of information. When the size of a particular pie is limited, however, as when new oil and gas exploration rights are to be auctioned off, companies hoard their information and the system works inefficiently.

Co-operation takes other forms as well. Most important is the joint-venture operation, which has become the predominant mode of conducting exploration plays for the independents in western Canada and for the majors in the frontier areas. In a joint venture, a number of companies pool a portion of their resources, primarily capital, and participate jointly in exploring a new prospect. One company acts as the operator for the group, and each receives a share in any eventual revenues proportional to its investment. Joint ventures serve many purposes. For companies with contiguous land holdings, they rationalize exploration over the whole area. For small companies, they permit participation in plays that would otherwise be too expensive. For many, as in the Eastcan consortium of seven companies drilling off Labrador, they provide the chance to learn about the technological and other problems associated with a new frontier. But for all companies, from the smallest to the largest, their main function is to spread the risks of petroleum exploration. The companies like to spread their exploration eggs among numerous drilling baskets. If, for example, there were one chance in ten that a wildcat well would produce oil or gas, a single failure could bankrupt a small company and, at $5 million to $10 million a well in the Arctic, strain the short-run finances of a major. Spreading one's capital among ten wells, however, greatly improves the chances of finding a "gusher".[15] Better to be a small participant in a large producer, than a full-time participant in a dry hole. The majors, which can afford to drill many wells and thereby spread their risks on their own, often begin a new play by themselves. If they have an early success, they will continue on their own. If the first few wells fail, they may then call in joint-venture partners to continue the play. For longer-term co-operation, the partners may form a consortium which develops its own operating staff. Panarctic in the Arctic islands, and Eastcan off the east coast are important consortiums in Canada's energy scene.

In production, unitization schemes call for similar kinds of inter-company co-operation. Since these are sanctioned, even required, by the various energy conservation boards, they give a legitimacy to inter-company agreements that is absent from most industries. All these forms of co-operation and deal-making call for extensive social interaction among oilmen from different companies. This reinforces business solidarity within the oil community and spills over into the non-business social lives of Calgary oilmen. Leisure-time interaction then feeds back upon business contact helping to preserve its intensity, informality, and enjoyment.

THE ROLE OF INFORMAL BUSINESS CONTACTS AND SOCIABILITY

If deal-making and information exchanges have an economic base, the social interaction to which they give rise takes on its own dynamic and further strengthens economic co-operation. In Calgary, the oil industry's sense of community is reinforced by local urban geography. In contrast to Australia where operations centres are scattered among various cities, Aberdeen where the oil community is not integrated with the permanent local community, or even Houston where the sheer vastness of the industry has caused it to sprawl to suburban satellites, Calgary's oil companies are mainly situated in the downtown core of the city, which is dominated by the oil companies' high-rise office buildings. Oilmen, their regulatory bodies, and their clubs and professional associations are all located within a few blocks of each other.[16] During business hours and at lunchtimes this area is a beehive of activity—of deal-making, information exchanging, business talk, and more relaxed socializing. Oilmen feel that their situation is unique in this regard.

> I should point out that there is quite a different community spirit in the western-Canadian oil industry than what you would find, say, in Toronto. In Toronto, it's sort of individual large companies. The fact that they may be in oil and gas really has no bearing on their relations with their counterparts. There's no special community amongst them, they seem to be lost in the over-all picture. But in western Canada, the oil industry is a community builder.

This special sense of community is further strengthened by common ties to the past. Senior oilmen are those who have grown up with the industry since Leduc. Many of them have shared experiences during the early exploration phase in western Canada, when times were rough, equipment and communications were less sophisticated, and young men had to earn their spurs in the field before they were granted softer office jobs in Calgary. This shared past cements present relations among senior oilmen and has induced a sense of mutual trust which allows them to conduct current business transactions in a strikingly informal way.

> People in the oil business spend money on a man's word. It's probably the only business in the world where a million-dollar well is drilled and there are no signed papers. It used to be practically every well twenty years ago; you never got the paper signed until months and months after. We still get it. Somebody will phone me up and say: "We are going to drill a well and we need another 12 per cent interest. It will probably cost you $25,000, and it's the best geological prospect I've seen in a long time." And I say: "Fine, count us in, and send us the paper." Well, the next thing I know the well's spudded and I say: "How about some paper, Joe?" and then Joe would get it.[17] As far as I know, that doesn't happen in any other business in the world.[18]

This kind of informality is still common, although less so than it used to be. Senior oilmen now compete with a younger generation who are, to some extent, a new breed. They spend less time in the field and more time with the computer, and many have received some training in modern management and accounting techniques. They may insist upon more formal contracts. Centralized accounting and communications techniques have also allowed corporate head offices to exert more control over local deal-making and to require the paper work to be in order before the well is spudded.

Calgary oilmen also claim that their industry has become fairly "clean" over the years, although it was well known that some shady wheeling and dealing went on during the early years.

> When I first came to Calgary, my impression was that certain companies and certain families prominent in the business here in town were skating very close to the edge. There was padding of public reports in terms of what would be coming in on wells to push up share prices and that sort of thing. The general scuttlebutt

around the streets at that time was that certain companies were overestimating reserves, the purpose of which was to push up share prices.

Today, within the established oil community, a person's reputation is too valuable an asset to jeopardize through shady dealing, at least at the expense of other oilmen.

The oil business is relatively free of graft, it's free of sharp dealers. You are gambling a lot of money so, well, if anybody backs out on his word in the oil business it becomes a closed shop to him, he's never going to make another deal.

A few interviewees admitted that illegal stock promotion still goes on, but claimed that it was mainly instigated by eastern-Canadian financiers, not western oilmen!

The oil community indulges in a great deal of informal social activity—daily lunches at the Petroleum Club and the Professional Club; shared recreational activities like skiing, curling, golf, and tennis; annual outings and parties for various companies and professional associations; and much informal visiting in each other's homes (which are concentrated in a few upper- and middle-class residential areas). It is tempting for a sociologist to overemphasize the role of socializing in business life. Expense-account living is no doubt partly a form of conspicuous consumption, and currying favour with top executives on the golf course may help further a few careers (see Dalton, 1959: 152 – 58). But, in the oil industry at least, informal social activities have a more important function in humanizing what would otherwise be an unbearably impersonal world of work. Particularly for the service companies, consultants, and small deal-making oil companies, informal socializing is something that they must take part in to succeed. For what people sell is not only a product, although the quality of the product is important, but also congenial social relations. Pure unmitigated selling would be too impersonal and unnatural—it might fit with uninformed negative stereotypes of businessmen, but not businessmen as the real people they are. In other words, social events *personalize* business life and make it pleasureable.

If business is a game that people play with varying degrees of success, enjoyment comes as much from the fun of the game and from the easy sociability with others that the game allows as from success itself. Business lunches provide the locker-room chatter of the game, or the English cricketer's afternoon tea break. Taking a client to lunch is not just a ploy for selling him a new type of drilling recorder. It *is* a technique for confirming your mutual membership in the oil community, and of assuring yourselves that you share interests and values. In this way, you become people for one another, you enjoy each other's company. The sale of the drilling recorder then follows comfortably, naturally, and sociably. It becomes a personal exchange rather than just a market exchange.

> To be seen at a number of social functions helps your business, there's no doubt about that. We like to do all our advertising by personal contact. There are certainly a lot of social functions here in Calgary, particularly within the oil community. The Oilfield Technical Society is one example, they will have dances and barbecues and things like this and, of course, being in the service business, what we do is phone John Doe, a customer, and invite him and his wife to come to the spring dance. There is a lot of that type of social contact. It's expensive; service companies invest a lot of money in that. But it's enjoyable, I won't say it isn't. There are all the favourite watering holes and a lot of meetings and conventions. We have some club memberships, this is part of the thing that goes with your job. Everybody, even our field people, have good expense accounts; they usually act wisely with them. You know, if you are making money and keeping your customers happy, you have to spend some money on them to do it. There is going to be a certain amount of wining and dining whether it's a toolpusher out in the field or the president of the company here in Calgary. Everybody has to be looked after. It's very difficult selling without a lot of personal contact. You will sell a certain amount making office calls, but you will do much better if you take the man out to lunch or you may take him and his wife out to dinner. Mind you, if we go out for a social evening, my wife and I with a customer, business is the last thing that comes to mind. It's strictly an entertainment feature and that's it.

"And that's it," but not quite. Sales follow smoothly along the tracks laid down by congenial social relations.

Business lunches differ from social evenings in that they are legitimately part of the work day, and business talk is permitted. They are useful for "feeling out" a potential customer or partner on a deal. Each person can hear the other's views, and can give and form initial impressions about whether a more formal deal may culminate later in their offices, or their law-yers' offices. Typically, by the end of the lunch the ground has been cleared but neither side is committed to anything; both agree to talk about it within their respective companies, and they expect to make contact again soon. Thus, the social occa-sion smoothes the way to a business deal and reduces the material crassness of a pure economic transaction. It also con-tributes to the flexibility with which the industry operates.

CONCLUSION: THE FLEXIBILITY OF THE CANADIAN OIL INDUSTRY

These main features—the dominant position of the majors, symbiotic inequality between the majors and other companies, the imperatives of competition, the advantages of co-operation, and the role of informal socializing in smoothing business transactions—are an integral part of the social organization of the oil industry in Calgary. However, if a single term could be used to describe such a complex structure, that term must surely be "flexible". Under the experienced direction of the major companies, the oil industry has evolved into a highly flexible and adaptable mode of socioeconomic organization.[19]

Although they do not have things all their own way, the majors, as the main architects, have designed a system that serves their purposes nicely. Through assigning work to smaller, less-powerful companies on a contract basis, they min-imize their own overhead costs, particularly the costs of carry-ing a large manual work force, and maximize the rates at which supplies and services of various kinds can be mobilized for their operations. Moreover, the system creates a buffer zone between them and the vicissitudes of the marketplace and political arena. When exploration and business activity pick up, they hire more service companies, drilling companies, and consultants. They do not hire large numbers of new permanent staff. When activity declines, they simply let contracts run out without signing new ones. This removes the need either to overburden themselves with excess manpower during lean peri-ods or to indulge in large-scale layoffs and firings which are unpleasant, bad for the public image, and detrimental to other employees' morale.

The burden of absorbing market, politically imposed, and seasonal fluctuations falls upon the auxiliary companies. The drilling companies in particular experience a perennial man-power problem. Ultimately, in the worst capitalist tradition, the burden is shifted to the shoulders of the workers—in this in-stance the itinerant roughnecks that one drilling company pres-ident correctly, if unfeelingly, described as "just a big labour pool". To succeed, drilling companies maximize the rates at which their rigs are used. For example, rigs may be used by different oil companies within a particular geographical area so that, most of the time, they do not have to be transported large distances at huge expense between contracts. This type of flexi-bility contributes to the efficiency of the system. Service-and-supply companies, consultants, and small oil companies also suffer more than the majors during slowdowns. For them, however, the costs of leaving the business are comparatively low; or the companies can remain dormant for a few years while their entrepreneurs seek opportunities in other fields.

The other organizational features also encourage flexibility. Competition spurs both the development of new kinds of ex-ploration and production techniques and the exploratory drill-ing of small and marginal reserves. The free flow of up-to-date information permits last-minute adjustments to exploratory and drilling programs. Joint ventures and the initiative of deal-making consultants and small entrepreneurs promote innova-tive business deals for continued exploration activity under a variety of geographical, economic, and political conditions.

This system is, oilmen insist, beneficial to Canada. Oil and gas are found and produced efficiently and effectively. The discipline of competition ensures that this is accomplished with minimal costs to the national economy.[20] Although economic self-interest does come into it, it is their faith in the value and efficiency of the present system that best explains the oilmen's heated opposition to change, and particularly to increased gov-ernment participation. The concept of a single, monolithic na-tional oil company is anathema to them because of the inflexi-bility, inefficiency, and bureaucratic wastefulness that they claim it would entail. Before assessing the last part of this claim, we need to know more about the internal organization of the major oil companies. Are they not, themselves, large inflexible bureaucracies?

CHAPTER FOUR

Inside a Major

Despite the dazzling variety of companies that make up the industry, most oilmen today work as employees of large multinational corporations. They are organization men; although they are *not* the faceless automatons depicted by social critics in the 1950s (Mills, 1951; Whyte, 1956; Reisman, 1961). Their work is not restricted to the mechanical exercise of a formally prescribed routine, but is rather task-oriented and involves continual attempts to solve challenging technical, administrative, and entrepreneurial puzzles.[1] In other words, oil companies are not bureaucracies in the classical sense (Weber, 1947). On the other hand, they are not the loose, constantly changing ad-hocracies depicted by Alvin Toffler either (1970: 124 – 51).

In this chapter, attention shifts from the oil industry as a whole to the internal organization of the Canadian majors.[2] These constitute the main unit in the larger system, and our organizational analysis must include a consideration of the principles that govern their internal operations. The genius of the contemporary corporation, I will argue, has been in its over-all success in maintaining a massive organization while, at the same time, making optimum use of individual and group skills at the micro level.[3] Again, flexibility and adaptability, of both the organization and its members, are key terms in the analysis. This reconciliation of the seemingly mutually exclusive demands of the corporation and the individual has involved a decentralization of the decision-making process *combined with* centralized, hierarchical control of the "ultimate say" about major corporate decisions. The system also has its internal costs, which show up in its callous treatment of those employees who fail to develop the skill flexibility required for successful adaptation to organizational needs.

ORGANIZATION AND ECONOMIC SUCCESS

The social organization of the modern corporation has evolved in response to an underlying economic imperative, and to understand its workings in a broader sociological sense we must first view them in this narrower economic sense. The competitive struggle for profits and growth has spurred four organizational innovations which have become institutionalized in the major oil companies, and which underlie their economic efficiency, effectiveness, and success.[4] These principles are the internal mobilization of capital, transnational technology, local manpower recruitment with internal training, and the collectivization of entrepreneurship.

Most Canadian majors, including the biggest, began as independent Canadian companies, but were eventually bought out by the international majors. The key to this sell-out was capital. In an international, free-enterprise system, and with no significant government protection, Canadian companies simply could not compete with their larger rivals from the United States. Imperial Oil, for example, was founded by Canadians in 1880 and might possibly have been able to survive as a small, independent Canadian company. But to maintain its position as the country's largest oil company, it had to find a secure source of large amounts of capital. It solved its capital-shortage problem by selling a majority interest to the Standard Oil Company—now Exxon (Campbell, 1971). This allowed Imperial, which continues to think of itself as a Canadian company, to break into the big leagues of modern industry, and was perhaps the only way in which it could have accomplished this at the time. Today, it is financially self-sufficient. It finances its ordinary exploration-and-development expansion through retained earnings, and turns to financial markets for extraordinary expenses like its investment in the Syncrude consortium set up to produce oil from the Alberta tar sands. This financial strength is central to the company's economic power in dealing with other companies and governments. More recently, other companies have followed Imperial's lead, with McColl – Frontenac selling out to Texaco, British American Oil Limited to Gulf, and Canadian Oil Companies to Shell. Although the Canadian identity of these subsidiaries has been more completely effaced than Imperial's, they share with Imperial their coming of age as mature corporations in their own right. The main cost of this development to Canada is that these subsidiaries pay out in dividends many millions of dollars annually to their foreign parents.

Oilmen employed by the Canadian majors claim that the single greatest advantage of their affiliation with their parents is immediate access to the latest technological advances of the multinationals' numerous and far-flung research laboratories. In terms of technological development and access, the multinational oil corporation is a single world-wide organization, *trans-*national rather than international. The parent company and its subsidiaries form a single technological pool which is basic to their strength and economic effectiveness. Canada obviously gains by having access to this technology, but the price is high. There is very little basic industrial research conducted within Canada (Cordell, 1971).

In the early years of the Alberta oil industry, following the discovery of the Leduc oil field in 1947, many positions within the Canadian majors were held by foreigners, mainly Americans. Over the years, however, the industry has become Canadianized in its personnel (see Table 1:3, p. 7). Underlying this trend are the manpower strategies of multinational oil companies. They rely upon a constant source of professionals in geology, engineering, accounting, and business administration. Since this type of manpower is in chronic short supply, the multinationals recruit locally where possible. Canada, with its cultural similarity to the United States and its well-developed system of higher education, is ideally suited to corporate needs in this regard.

Mutual benefits accrue from the second aspect of corporate manpower development as well—that is, the elaborate in-house training programs that major oil companies provide for their professional workers and promising administrators. University degrees in engineering or geology mean that the people holding them have proven their likely potential for useful work in the industry. The corporation itself undertakes to mould them into oilmen—or rather, it provides opportunities for them to develop into one or other of a diversity of types of oilmen, all of which can make a valuable contribution to the corporation. Nearly all the managers and professionals interviewed reported that, during their early years with their companies, they had been on training programs and assignments to Houston, London, and other international oil centres. This policy of in-house manpower training also helps the company to supply new needs as they arise. The following account illustrates how changing technology calls for flexible, adaptable people.

> I graduated in mining, not oil geology. Imperial said: "No, that's fine, we'll teach you anything you have to know." I've found that in this dynamic change in technology all the time, the biggest asset you can have is an open mind. As an example of that, what happens to me, a mining geologist within an oil company, is that I've progressed up the ladder to become a computer expert! They tested us for computer aptitude and I scored very high and right away they asked me if I would like to go into the computer game, and try to solve geological problems with a computer. I said: "Hell! Why not?"

Entrepreneurship has generally been seen as an attribute of individuals (Schumpeter, 1951; Galbraith, 1971; Chandler, 1962), while more strictly sociological commentators have suggested that it should be viewed as an aspect of a social role (Belshaw, 1955; Barth, 1963). I would like to add the further suggestion that entrepreneurship can become collectivized and institutionalized, and that indeed this process has been central to the economic success of modern corporations. No individual entrepreneur could mobilize people and resources for, say, drilling a new petroleum prospect on Sable Island with anything like the intelligence and efficiency of a co-ordinated group of professionals with expertise in deciding whether, when, where, and how to drill. A large oil company like Shell Canada *is* such a co-ordinated collectivity; the corporation is the entrepreneur. Executives in the Canadian majors are not simply pawns of their parent head-offices (Levitt, 1970), but are very much involved as entrepreneurial co-ordinators in the decision-making process.

These organizational principles—internal financing, transnational technological development, local recruitment and in-house training of manpower, and the collectivization of entrepreneurship—underly the purely economic success of the major oil companies. Our focus shifts now to the organizational form through which these principles operate.

THE CORE STRUCTURE

At the industry level we have seen how, over the years, the major oil companies have worked out a way both to maintain dominance and to allow for much flexibility and adaptability in the everyday operations of the industry. They maintain over-all financial, technological, and decision-making control, but contract out most of the routine and less-rewarding work to hundreds of small companies of various types. This same combination of ultimate central control and lower-level flexibility has also become part of the internal structure of the majors. Local departments in Calgary, or at least sections and subsections of departments, are assigned tasks by the company (that is, by its executives and managers who perform the co-ordinating function), and their members are paid for performing the tasks. The parallel between internal and external relations is striking when one considers that many activities which were once performed by departments of the companies, such as drilling and geophysical exploration, are now done on a contract basis with outside firms. The boundary between company and environment is shifting and unstable.

There are, however, important differences. Unlike contract workers, employees are paid a salary and continue to enjoy job security when they complete a task. Further, and this is the main reason why there is a limit to what can be contracted out, professional workers provide the pool from which new managerial talent is recruited. Core activities such as geological/geophysical interpretation and reservoir engineering continue to be performed by groups that are part of the organization of the company. These primary groups, with their shifting tasks and changing memberships, are the basic units of oil companies as organizations.

Nevertheless, these organizations are not amorphous. They have a core structure that is stable and persistent. This core structure is determined by three kinds of imperatives: technical, business-administrative, and occupational. The technical imperative is universal to the oil industry in all types of social systems. Even a small Calgary company has a formal organization that includes a geologist in charge of exploration, an engineer in charge of production, and a manager who co-ordinates the activities of the two. (Two or three of these roles may, of course, be performed by the same individual.) As companies become larger, these roles become departments, and these in turn become differentiated into sections that deal with specialized technical activities such as geophysical interpretation and reservoir simulation; and co-ordination becomes necessary within as well as between departments (See Figure 4:1).

FIGURE 4:1   Core Structure of an Exploration and Production Company

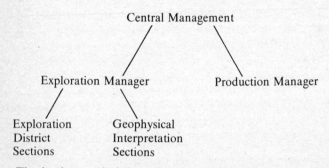

The business-administrative imperative refers to the fact that oil companies are privately owned capitalist enterprises oriented to making profits. This means that they come to include departments of financial experts, accountants, economic planners, and legal advisors. For the Canadian majors, most such personnel are located in the head offices in central Canada. They have important indirect effects upon corporate decisions about whether or not technically feasible proposals will be accepted and acted upon.

The occupational imperative is related to the technical one. It has emerged as a kind of social convention within the majors that only those employees with professional qualifications are regarded as potential managers. This creates an almost impassable mobility barrier for non-professional workers in the oil industry, and a dual hierarchy within the companies—with one side related to field operations and one to office operations (see Figure 4:2). Among professional workers, a further distinction is made between a technical and an administrative ladder, although all agree that the highest rungs of the latter reach far above those of the former (see Figure 4:2).

In terms of the above formulation, the roles of senior-level managers and executive officers are shaped by these three

FIGURE 4:2   Administrative Hierarchies and Mobility Barriers

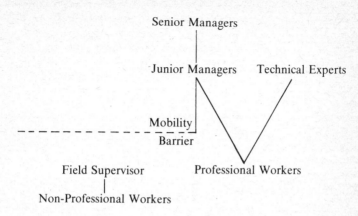

imperatives. They must have professional qualifications, and usually move from the technical to the administrative ladder after showing leadership ability within various technical work groups. Their main tasks are to co-ordinate the activities of the various technical departments and to manage their relations with the more business-oriented ones. They are also the leaders for entrepreneurial decision-making about over-all company strategy and expansion. As they move up the administrative ladder, they become more directly influenced by the business imperative, and less by the technical. Membership of the board of directors of a Canadian subsidiary is a business appointment made to fulfil a legal requirement. Since the majority of shares are owned by the foreign parents, it is meaningless to suggest that directors are elected by the shareholders. Rather, they are appointed by the parent on the advice of current board members and senior managers. They may be used as a liaison between the parent and the Canadian subsidiary and between the company and the wider business and professional community. But they have little influence upon the daily operations of the Canadian majors.

TASK-CENTRED ORGANIZATION

The behaviour of non-managerial professionals within the oil industry is organized in terms of group tasks rather than individual offices. Individuals are assigned to groups that work on projects of varying types and durations. Within an exploration department, for example, projects may range from a short-term job involing reassessment of the geology of an oil well in Alberta which has started producing salt water to a long-term assignment such as finding and recommending good drilling prospects in the Beaufort Sea. The groups are usually small and represent varying types of expertise. They are co-ordinated by a supervisor who represents the first level of management for the professional workers. Individuals are shifted into and out of different groups either for training purposes or because their particular expertise is needed. The boundaries of the groups are amorphous and shifting, as the supervisor calls upon other expertise in the department for help with specific problems, and as people are assigned to or leave the groups on a temporary basis. The following comments describe this work milieu from the point of view of those involved.

> We go on from project to project. It all depends where the need is. On this Beaufort task force, we work as a group—a special-technique group working on the various problems, and we have geologists and geophysicists involved in that. Right now I have two other projects and if something else should come up, I'll drop these, because they don't have as much priority. That applies to almost all the professionals in this office, we juggle things around. We have been able to keep more or less the same people on the projects, but if we made a deal with someone in a new area and all of a sudden there was a discovery in that area, well, we'd probably allocate people to it—pull them off this project or another project that is not currently hot.

This flexible form of organization calls for flexible people. As technologies change and as individuals move around in response to changing organizational needs they develop new skills and find new applications for old ones. Formal job descriptions have little meaning ("Well, they call me a senior engineer, but what I'm *really* involved in is. . . . "); and there is no clear-cut division of labour. At Imperial, for example, the distinction between geologist and geophysicist is so unclear that they are moving towards the general label "explorationist". The trick for career success is to become not so much a technical specialist, as a technical generalist, one who can apply technical knowledge to new problems, and who can quickly pick up new technologies. This both allows a great deal of autonomy to professional workers in their day-to-day activities and creates control problems for management. The successful manager does not prescribe how tasks should be done, but instead skilfully mobilizes the manpower expertise at his command for the various projects as they emerge. Recently, corporate administrators have attempted to give formal recognition to this control-of-professional-experts problem through a technique of "management by objectives". Employees are assigned objectives, but are free to work out their own means of achieving them. The weakness of this approach, in the oil industry at least, is that the objectives themselves keep changing.

We should also note an important sociological implication of this group-project mode of organization: it mitigates the supposed anonymity and impersonality of working for a large organization.

> I'm not at all bothered by being a member of a large organization. Actually, I think of myself more as a member of the frontier exploration group which is not a big organization. You know, the company is highly compartmentalized. When I was in geophysical research I thought of myself as part of geophysical research—a couple of dozen people, we were pretty independent. Every now and then I'd get shipped off to Houston for a couple of weeks, and then I'd think: "My God, this is a big organization." But most of the time you're just involved with what your group is doing.

Not all oilmen agree with this, and many leave to join small companies because they feel lost within a big organization. Part of their feeling has to do with their limited access to information about what "the company" is doing. This points to another perennial problem for managers and workers alike.

INFORMATION CONTROL AND COMMUNICATION

The flexibility of daily operations within a major oil company appears to reflect the way the industry as a whole operates. So too with information. The problem of information control at the industry level compounds the usual information and communications difficulties typically found within large organizations (Blau and Scott, 1962: 116 – 39). We have seen that information is a key intermediate resource within the oil industry, and that companies attempt to keep certain information secret, both to gain a short-term technological advantage and to compete for land. The companies are highly security conscious and carefully check up on and monitor all visitors to their plants and office buildings.

This concern for security extends to company employees, and senior management feel a strong inclination to keep sensitive information secret from their own more junior personnel, for fear of an information leak. On the other hand, professional workers are naturally curious about their company's operations, feel that they deserve to be trusted with information, and are critical and resentful if it is kept from them. This feeling is captured in the following comment in which an employee of one major company criticizes another major:

> I've heard that _____ are so obsessed with security that they take a fellow, a PHD, put him in an office, and give him work to do, but they won't tell him what he's going to do. He'll have to use his brain to solve certain problems, but they won't give him the big picture because they feel this could lead to breaches in security. I could never tolerate that, it would be like being on a conveyer belt.

This is probably an overstatement. The major companies cannot afford to keep too much from their professional workers who do indeed need to view the larger picture to do good work on most projects, and who, if they become dissatisfied, can easily leave to work for other companies.

In keeping with its flexible form of organization, information *within* a department tends to flow fairly smoothly, largely through informal channels—members call it an "open-door policy". People communicate freely with their fellow workers, supervisors, and managers whenever they want to pass on or obtain information related to their projects. Information is also communicated to more senior levels more formally during weekly departmental meetings, when representatives from selected task groups are invited to present accounts of their projects' progress and problems. These are important occasions for ambitious workers, as they give them their best opportunities to impress management.

Information flow between departments, and from higher to

lower organizational levels is more of a problem. Managers of staff groups that perform service functions for the line groups, in particular, tend to complain of being excluded from the main flow of information.

> Occasionally, something falls through the crack because of the exploration district manager's not realizing what the capabilities of our (service) department are. Communication with district managers has been a significant problem. Fundamentally, it's a question of the abilities of the various people involved to assimilate and correlate all the information that is necessary. It's completely impossible to maintain contact on a routine basis with 108 people, so I have to rely on the communications of the supervisors of each section. That means, of course, that since my section heads don't have direct access to the management group, it largely falls upon me to communicate the objectives of the districts to my section heads. So it gets to be quite a long chain of communication.

Information from the top can be conceived as part of a redistributive exchange system (Sahlins, 1965). Information flows from the periphery to the centre, and is then redistributed from the centre to the periphery—in the present organizational metaphor, from the top to the bottom. In this process, the top controls how much and what type of information is allowed to flow to whom. Strategies tend to change over time in response to the opposing claims of security and employee satisfaction. A security leak may be followed by a period of tight control, while periods when information flows relatively freely may be induced by employee pressure. Imperial, for example, recently instituted a program of regular written reviews of its production and exploration plans for distribution to its professional employees in response to the latter's requests. This combination of project-group flexibility and overall centralized control of the flow of information has its parallel in the decision-making processes of the major oil companies.

COLLECTIVE DECISION-MAKING WITH CENTRALIZED CONTROL

The histories of the major oil companies have been marked by apparently contradictory periods of centralization and decentralization (Chandler, 1962). At present the big companies differ in their degree of centralization, with Texaco retaining tighter head-office control than, say, Exxon or Gulf. This lack of uniformity reflects a basic dilemma that the leaders of multinational corporations face: they must keep the organization sensitive to local conditions and offer satisfying work for employees while maintaining control and co-ordinating the company's operations at head office. The major oil companies, with long international experience and large staffs of professional workers who tend to resist militaristic bureaucratic control (Vollmer and Mills, 1966: 264–94), have managed partially to resolve this dilemma.

The key to this resolution has been an implicit recognition of the difference between the *process* of decision-making and the ultimate *control* over what decisions are made and what action is to be taken. Within the oil corporations, decision-making has become decentralized; or, more accurately, it has become *collectivized*, so that employees at low organizational levels—professional workers and local branch-plant managers—take an active and formative part in the decision-making process. This development is not contrary to the interests of head-office executives and directors. Rather, it makes for more informed and, therefore, more intelligent decisions, which is to their advantage and helps account for the economic success of these corporations. However, senior personnel at head office do maintain ultimate control, and modern methods of transportation and communication have allowed them to enhance this control in recent years. Imperial's senior officials regularly commute among Toronto, Calgary, New York, and Houston, while direct telephone and teletype connections keep them in constant contact with branch-plant operations, and in daily touch, even, with the progress of wells being drilled in the remote Arctic. The international oil companies might serve as models for McLuhan's theory of the global village (or rather, as a number of competing "global-villages" [1964]).

This formulation helps account for what seems at first to be a contradiction in our empirical data on the oil industry in Calgary. On the one hand, it is objectively apparent (and oilmen agree) that the control over the activities of the Canadian majors in recent years has become more centralized. On the other hand, professional oilmen at all organizational levels claim both to be involved in the decision-making process, and to be satisfied with the degree of their involvement, although they do not actually make many final decisions by themselves.

Our survey data for the industry sample suggest that, as we would expect, employees at lower organizational levels make fewer decisions than do those at higher levels about hiring, firing, and promoting employees as well as about how the organization should be run. On the other hand, there is very little correlation between organizational level and degree of job formalization, either in terms of job codification or in terms of imposition of structure. And, subjectively, professional workers do not *feel* markedly more powerless than supervisors and managers.[5] This suggests that, although managers make most of the decisions about employees and about the organization, most professional workers enjoy a fair degree of autonomy in deciding how their jobs should be done, and this is the crucial factor in determining how powerless they feel. These data are supported by our findings from personal interviews, and it is to these that we must turn for an analysis of the context that underlies the survey's findings.

Centralization at Imperial can be taken as paradigmatic for the industry. During the past decade, exploration and production operations have been centralized in two stages: first small regional offices in provincial centres such as Regina and Dawson Creek were moved into Calgary and Edmonton; and then most of the Edmonton-based operations were relocated to Calgary. These moves were accompanied by a streamlining of the departments' formal organization, which induced some short-term resentment and conflict among personnel who were given new positions with less authority and autonomy. At the same time, corporate lines to the Toronto head office were made firmer and more direct. The exploration manager in Calgary now reports directly to an executive vice-president in charge of exploration, and the production manager to one in charge of production. There is no longer a regional manager of western-Canadian operations as such. The Calgary office and the Toronto office have become meshed in a single organizational structure, linked by continual communication.

This centralization is recognized as such by employees in Calgary, and, although there is some resentment by local managers over the decline in their autonomy, the centralization is generally viewed as legitimate for administrative and financial reasons.

I don't think there is any autonomy any more. Years ago they used to operate by delegating the authority, having offices in different towns, and of course it was very decentralized. From the time we started working in the frontiers it's been much more obvious that your day-to-day decisions were million-dollar decisions that senior people in the company would have to be involved in. My role (as supervisor) is not so much that of a decision-maker, but more or less a supervisor of the technical interpretation, and that of communicating the results of the data interpretation to the decision-makers. I think this change is inevitable, it doesn't bother me, although it does bother a lot of people.

There is also a feeling among employees in Alberta (denied by senior managers in Toronto) that the centralization has extended further—to Exxon's control over Imperial.

Despite this centralization, Imperial's professional workers in Calgary continue to enjoy a great deal of autonomy in carrying out their projects; and for most this appears to be the more important consideration. The following comment is by a geophysical interpreter:

I'm on my own almost all the time. I decide on something I want to do and, if it's going to cost a lot of money I sort of tell him (the supervisor) what I think should be done. Unless it's a preposterously stupid idea, he says to carry on until I come up with my maps and present them, and since I've been involved with a given area, nobody is really going to know this better than I. I've been to a lot of these reviews [meetings with management], and there's a lot of vigorous discussion on certain interpretations, but you're not really shot down too often.

This comment indicates how autonomy is built into technological specialization and competence. Managers acknowledge this: "I know very little about well-site operations for example, but, like most managers, I rely upon the key people who know what they're talking about." One of these "key people" expressed his view of the decision-making process as follows: "I think a lot of the ideas. We sort of generate the ideas and present them on up, and I think I have enough say."[6] In this process, senior-level managers monitor and co-ordinate decision-making input as it is presented to them, and have the power and responsibility of the final say in major decisions.

The board of directors and the parent corporation serve as the final assessors of these collectively reached proposals and decisions. As Imperial's chief executive officer put it: "It isn't Exxon saying 'Now this is what we're going to do.' It's Imperial saying 'Here's what we propose to do and what suggestions do you have to make?'"

Successful corporate managers in the oil industry, then, do not dictate procedures and detailed regulations for their professional workers. Such a mode of operation would be frustrating to the workers and inefficient for the companies. Instead, successful managers are like successful coaches in sports. They are able to put together good teams, to recognize talent and reward it, to co-ordinate technical advice with economic and financial advice, and to take the ultimate responsibility for the team's successes and failures. In doing this, they exercise economic power and enjoy the lucrative salaries, fringe benefits, and prestige that capitalist corporate leaders provide for themselves. In this, they are generally supported by the organizations' members.

LEGITIMATE OLIGARCHY

In their internal political organization, the Canadian majors are self-perpetuating oligarchies. Ultimate decision-making power rests with a few corporate executives in the central-Canadian head offices. They are appointed, not elected, and effectively enjoy tenure of office until retirement. Furthermore, they enjoy the privilege of appointing their own successors. Invariably, these are people like themselves, men who have worked their way up the corporate hierarchy from professional worker through junior-level to senior-level managerial positions. They are also similar socially—white, Anglo-Saxon Canadians from mainly middle-class backgrounds. And they tend to think alike. In particular, they believe in the "free-enterprise" system and in the need to defend that system from popular and governmental encroachment.[7]

Such a system is clearly contradictory to the democratic ideals ostensibly held in most Western countries, as both liberal and radical critics of corporate capitalism have been pointing out for some time (Berle and Means, 1932; Baran and Sweezy, 1963; Mills, 1956). Yet, with almost no exceptions, the professional workers and lower-level administrators who work for these organizations in Calgary completely accept the system's legitimacy. Why is this acceptance so nearly complete?

I will deal with secondary reasons first, some of which we have touched upon in passing, and some of which we will deal with in more detail in later chapters. Oilmen, for the most part, believe that they enjoy a large measure of autonomy in their work, and that they have a real input into corporate decision-making. They enjoy their work for its intrinsic value, and because it provides them as well with a good income and a prestigious position within the local community. For many, their career aspirations entail commitment to the given system, since their ultimate aim is to gain entry into the corporate oligarchy themselves. Furthermore, their belief in private enterprise usually means that they feel fairly comfortable with the way its corporate units are organized.

The real reason why this oligarchic structure has legitimacy in the eyes of its members, however, is that the oilmen believe that it works. This belief is reinforced when they compare the system with what they perceive as the bureaucratic inefficiency of government-run agencies and enterprises. Their industry, they feel, is effective and efficient in finding, producing, transporting, refining, and distributing petroleum and petroleum products. It therefore follows, in their view, that their industry is correctly organized. Within the majors, this faith is complemented by the more specific belief that, for the most part, people are promoted to prestigious positions because they deserve them.

There are some reservations. It is felt that some people do not get the recognition they deserve because of personality characteristics. They are too shy, or too inarticulate, or too modest to be "discovered" by top management. But, whereas most would agree that some talented people do not get the promotions they deserve, they would also agree that those who do get appointed to senior positions are talented people. A striking feature of the majors as organizations is the continual process of manpower assessment that goes on. This includes formal reviews through questionnaires, interviews, and training courses, as well as informal assessments in presentations to management and in the everyday work of the various project groups. Managers and workers assess their colleagues and themselves; and, generally speaking, senior managers' assessments agree with people's views about their colleagues and, ultimately, themselves. The following comments illustrate aspects of this legitimacy.

Corporation management is a lot better than government management, because, well, corporations can fire you, you don't get fired in the government. I think the way management here is chosen and promoted is good. I think they have very capable people in pretty well all their management positions.

I think the people that move up quickly are very ambitious and hard workers; but at the same time I think that our company . . . it's not one man's decision to say "Joe Blow over there should be here," it's more a committee assessment. I believe that the people they move on, they should be there. They've got the ability, I think. They can assess things and they can organize things, and they can express themselves.

These comments also imply another side to this process of legitimating assessment, especially since so many people are involved in the decision. What happens when one's colleagues (particularly subordinates) and oneself fail to measure up in the assessment?

THE CHANGING CORPORATE MORAL ORDER: PURGES AND DISPENSABLE MEN

The early years of the Alberta oil industry were characterized by a great deal of camaraderie and a shared *esprit de corps*. Within the major companies, particularly Imperial, this was reflected in close relations between "the company" and its employees. The company was proud to be in the forefront of a frontier industry and took a paternalistic and somewhat protective attitude towards its employees. In return for "an honest day's work", the employees enjoyed secure jobs, and many reciprocated with a strong sense of loyalty to the company.

A number of pressures have eroded this comfortable, almost personal, company-employee tie in recent years. Growth has meant increased size with less daily contact between senior management and professional workers. Competition from the other Canadian majors and independents has challenged Imperial's dominance, and the company has responded by adopting oligopolistic personnel policies. It attempts to match what competitors offer in terms of salaries and benefits rather than, as in former days, to maintain its image as a special kind of employer. And the pressures for centralization and adaptable manpower have made obsolete many of the skills and rendered redundant many of the services of a number of professional workers and managers, particularly older men who have grown up with the company.

In response to these various pressures, which were exacerbated by a mild recession in the industry in 1971, the company fired a number of long-term employees, some of them respected men in middle-level managerial and technical positions.[8] This "purge", as the employees call it, has had a tremendous impact, not only upon those laid off, but also upon organizational morale and upon the nature of company-employee relations.

The case of Mr. R. illustrates the personal trauma induced by the purge.[9] Mr. R., a Canadian, began his career in the oil industry with ten years' service in another foreign affiliate of Exxon, and started working with Imperial in the Leduc era. He eventually worked his way up to become a senior researcher at Imperial's laboratory in Calgary, and became known for his published papers and guest lectures in Houston. Suddenly, in 1971, he and six other employees in his group were told that they were being "retired early", as Exxon was planning to centralize the kind of research they were doing in Houston. In Mr. R.'s phrase, "the bottom fell out" of these men's lives. Some, including Mr. R., later found jobs with other companies, one man "has more or less given up", and another has "gone mental—he just lies in bed doing nothing". The men were given severance pay and reduced pensions, which were for less money than they expected and felt entitled to. One man threatened to sue the company, and purportedly received a substantial out-of-court settlement. Mr. R., a quiet, unassuming man, refused to sue. Initially, his earlier foreign experience was not recognized; but later it was, and his pension was increased.

For Mr. R. it was not so much the economic as the psychological shock that he found most difficult to adjust to. During his last days at Imperial, his social relations with long-term colleagues suddenly became strained and uncomfortable. Local managers were "scared" to do anything on his behalf, and even became "scared" to talk to him. He was particularly hurt that when he was to be awarded a pin for long-term service, a procedure usually done in person by a high-ranking manager, he was merely sent his in the mail by a secretary.

Other employees, particularly older ones, were also adversely affected by the purge, as they began to worry about their own welfare and future with the company.

> Oh, I guess it [the purge] certainly affected my view of things. I guess I thought it wasn't necessary, very poor. I suppose you relate these things to yourself, what will my situation be?

> It's a funny thing, I don't worry about it at all at work or at home; but when I go on holidays, I dream about it at night, of all things—stupid time to do it.

Many younger professional workers, however, and most managers felt that the lay-offs were, in principle at least, a good thing.

> I felt that it was a good thing, I really honestly felt that. There were people being let go who were not efficient, and who were in fact gouging the company and I resented the presence of those people throughout the company. So I said to myself this is a good thing, we're trying to preserve an environment where people can do good work. It was a question of somebody looking around and saying: "This g. d. operation is supporting a lot of people who are not pulling their weight, so if we want Imperial to go forward and be competitive, we must trim the tree."

There was general support for the sentiment that people who are not "pulling their weight" should be let go; but most workers and managers at Calgary felt that some mistakes had been made in the 1971 firings, that purges are bad for morale, that older employees who have served the company loyally for years should be "carried" to their normal retirement time even if their contribution of useful work has declined, and that letting people go should be a normal, continual part of operations rather than a series of periodic blood-letting purges.

From a wider perspective, the 1971 purge seems to have symbolized the culmination of a basic shift in company-employee relations at Imperial that reflects the organization's new demand for flexible manpower, for both technical and administrative generalists. This demand implies that those employees who cannot develop this flexibility, even if their failure is due to a trained incapacity acquired during an earlier era of industry operations, must be dismissed.

This attitude makes for more tenuous ties between the company and its employees; and for ambitious employees this weakening of ties is complemented by the career options that they see in consulting and small oil companies. Company-employee relations have become more pragmatic and impersonal than formerly; and this is in keeping with the emphasis on flexibility both in the industry as a whole and in its constituent companies. This new emphasis in company-employee relations has induced a new morality. Measured by the old moral code of mutual loyalty, the managers at Imperial have become, in Mr. R.'s term, "anomic". But a new breed of employees does not view the relationship as requiring mutual loyalty, and prefers the pragmatic career autonomy this allows them. A promising young manager explained it as follows:

> I must admit that the possibility of moving from the company has crossed my mind from time to time. There are opportunities within the industry, and I think there will be growing opportunities in the future with government, if one is interested. I'm quite open about it, I don't have any magic aura for the corporation. I can help them and they can help me, it's kind of a mutual thing, and on it goes. If I got very disenchanted, I'd talk it over with my management and make a cold, hard decision.

The new, pragmatic moral order at Imperial (which seems to be even more prevalent at the other Canadian majors) is like that of a large city, the old order like that of a small town. Some of the older employees, who recognize but feel ambivalent about the change, express the regret that, in their early careers, they may have been too concerned with job security and too loyal to the company. They seem to be reading the new morality back into the old situation.

CONCLUSION

The characteristic features of the social organization of the Canadian majors have emerged over the years in response first to the over-all organization of the Canadian oil industry, and

second to the internal requirements of the large oil corporations themselves. The majors are not simply products of their
environment, but, because of their dominant position, shape it
as much as they are shaped by it. Indeed, in this case at least,
it is unrealistic to try to unravel the cause-and-effect relations
between the companies as organizations and their industrial
environment. Rather, the internal organization of the majors
should be viewed as an integral part of the organization of the
industry.

The same imperatives apply to individual units as to the
industry as a whole. In this open-resource industry, the competitive struggle for profits and growth has given rise to a
flexible and adaptable form of organization, both at the industry and the company levels. The unstable boundary between
the two is part of this flexibility. Much of the majors' work is
done by contractors, who can be hired for a variety of jobs as
the need arises, while internally work is organized in terms of
flexible project groups with shifting tasks and changing memberships. Both these adaptations ensure that the majors can
mobilize optimum amounts of technical and business expertise
in their daily operations. Technical decison-making is left
largely to the contractors and project groups, with central management maintaining co-ordination and ultimate control.
Within the companies, decision-making is largely a collective
process. Managers co-ordinate this process, and their success
depends upon their ability to mobilize the manpower resources
at their disposal to take advantage of changing opportunities as
they emerge. Even at its lower levels, management is more
entrepreneurial and less mechanically administrative than bureaucratic models would suggest.

Effective economic power within the Canadian majors is
held by a central oligarchy of senior executives who appoint
their own successors. Appointments are made on the basis of
an elaborate and continual process of manpower training and
assessment. The public nature of this assessment process, in
which lower-level employees come to accept and apply the
same criteria in judging one another as do the senior executives, leads to the system's acquiring a high degree of legitimacy with the employees. Despite certain resentments, they
believe that their privileged and powerful organizational leaders are competent and, for the most part, fairly selected.

Unlike contractors, members of project groups are long-term salaried employees. This creates a "problem" for management when some employees, often because of a trained incapacity acquired during their earlier service to the company, fail to develop the kind of technical and administrative adaptability required by contemporary conditions. Imperial has attempted to resolve this dilemma by "purging" a number of senior people. This has been a psychologically traumatic experience for these victims, and has back-fired on the company by adversely affecting employee morale. More broadly, the purge has signalled a new era of pragmatic company-employee relations to replace the older more paternalistic and more personal ties of the early days in Alberta. Many of the younger employees prefer this arrangement for the limited commitment to the company and the career autonomy that it allows.

CHAPTER FIVE

Careers: The Luxury of Choice

The concept of "career" is a transition in our analysis as we move from the social organization of the industry to consider the social psychology of Canadian oilmen. On the one hand, it can further our understanding of the oilman's world; on the other, it can clarify the relationship between the social organization of the industry and the social psychology, satisfactions, beliefs, values, and ideology of the people who comprise it. A consideration of career can help bridge the theoretical gap between social processes and the formulation of beliefs and ideas that has plagued sociology since the work of Karl Mannheim and his critics (Mannheim, 1936; DeGré, 1941).

Essentially, the connection which I suggest exists between the social organization of the oil industry and the ideas of the people who comprise it is a dialectical one. Oilmen collectively and actively construct their world views in response to and in terms of their living experience within the industry, the organization of which confronts them as a reality to which they must adapt.[1] This experience and process of adaptation constitute their careers, which could be defined as the dialectical meeting place between objective and subjective social reality. On the one hand, careers can be viewed objectively in terms of the "chains of opportunity" and constraint that industry and corporate organizational structure provide (White, 1970); on the other hand, they can be viewed from the subjective perspective of the individual human beings who live those careers (Stebbins, 1970). In pursuing their careers, individuals make choices and exercise their free will, but the scope for such choices varies greatly among industries and occupations. The central claim made in this chapter is that the Canadian oil industry provides great opportunities for free choices in that it offers a variety of career options to its professional members. Later, I will argue that this luxury of career choice contributes greatly to the generally high level of job satisfaction within the industry, and helps account for oil-men's strong commitment to their industry and resistance to changes in its organization.

The body of this chapter consists of an ideal/typical description and analysis of the various career options and patterns that professional oilmen enjoy; and these in turn are contrasted with the more restricted opportunities of non-professionals within the industry. Towards the end, the discussion returns to the question of determinism, with the suggestion that, although industry organization sets the conditions for career patterns, these in turn exert a shaping influence upon some aspects of the organization.

PROFESSIONAL CAREER PATTERNS

The Initial Years

The typical Calgary oilman studies engineering or geology at a western-Canadian university.[2] He gets his first exposure to the oil industry by taking a summer job with a Canadian major, which usually involves some field experience, such as working in a gas-processing plant if he is an engineering student, with a seismic crew if he is a student in geophysics, or on a drilling rig if he is a geology student. Since the last two operations are done by contractors, he may act as a company representative although his main task is simply to gain some practical experience in the industry.

Upon graduation, the young professional goes to work for one of the Canadian majors (or a large independent), which, as we have seen, serve as the training centres of the industry. His first year is mainly a training year and may involve a trip to Houston or some other international oil centre for a course in some aspect of petroleum technology. He is then assigned to a technical task group. Initially, his task assignment involves some fairly mechanical operation such as geophysical processing, well-logging, or computer simulation of particular oil and gas reservoirs. Later, if he shows promise, he is assigned to more challenging technical work like geophysical interpretation or the design of secondary recovery methods for producing wells. If he shows leadership potential, he may become a group leader after a few years.

After working for four or five years in such a technical

capacity, the young oilman reaches a crucial phase of his career. On the basis of his own and other people's assessments of his abilities and of the career opportunities open to him, he must make a decision about what kind of long-term career he wants to pursue. There are numerous possibilities. If he decides to remain with his present company (a strikingly large number of Canadian oilmen have spent their whole careers with a single Canadian major), his basic choice is whether to opt for a technical or a managerial career.

Technical Careers

Technical careers appeal to people who like solving challenging technical problems, and who feel uncomfortable with having to co-ordinate and make decisions about personnel—to cope with "people problems" as oilmen put it. Successful professional technologists can enjoy interesting work, good salaries, job security, and a fair measure of prestige from those who depend upon their technical expertise. Technical careers themselves are of two types. Most professional technicians continue to work upon technical problems of immediate practical concern, such as where to drill the next well to best effect in the Beaufort Sea, or how to maximize recovery from a declining field in southern Saskatchewan. But some people shift to longer-term technical problems and are known as researchers. Imperial Oil runs a fairly large exploration and production research laboratory in Calgary which works on such problems as improving knowledge and expertise in ice engineering for the north, or finding the best means to recover the heavy oils from the Cold Lake region of Alberta. The following comments by a researcher illustrate aspects of the contingencies and satisfactions of those who opt for long-term technical careers within the majors.

> Immediately before I was here I was in graduate school. Before that I worked for three years in eastern Canada, as an engineer in a research lab. I came back to do my master's degree at the University of Alberta, and doctorate at the University of Calgary. Graduate degrees are helpful for getting into the research area but, as far as the work I'm doing goes, I'm not really using it that much. I applied to Imperial because I wanted to stay in Calgary where I could work while I finished off the degree. I prefer the west, I have

no desire whatsoever to go to Toronto. That means I probably can't go too far in the management line. I had no exposure at all to the oil industry before I came to Alberta for my master's and doctorate. That's definitely a disadvantage now when I'm dealing with production problems. Our major project is trying to investigate the thermal damage that can be done through permafrost, mainly in the Delta area; and we have done some design for possible gasplant development in the Delta area. We don't have one project as such, but are involved in a number of projects.

I guess I'll probably be here five years from now. I would guess my work would have something to do with Arctic development. If I did move, it would probably be as a consultant, but I don't think so, particularly with my lack of experience in the oil patch. In a big organization like Imperial, you get exposed to many people, conferences, meetings, trips; and there are an awful lot of support facilities to make the job much easier. And you have the freedom to work with the larger research group in Houston. These are conveniences you don't get in a smaller company. Of course, you can get lost in a big company, shuffled off into some job. . . . This doesn't happen too much, they keep moving people around.

This quote clearly illustrates the context within which oilmen make their choices. This man gained higher degrees to pursue a research career. He enjoys the technical challenges of his work, and sees that a big company can provide superior opportunities to be involved in frontier research with other experts and with the best possible support facilities. Despite the possibility that one might become lost in a big company, he prefers it to a small company which provides less technological challenge. He has thought about going into consulting work, but does not feel familiar enough with the Calgary oil community to take that career risk. And his decision not to move to Toronto means that he has effectively locked himself out of a managerial career.

Not all technical careers, however, are chosen from this wide a variety of options. Those whom management consider to be lacking in promise either as administrators or as high-level technical experts may be kept on for years doing the more routine kinds of geological, geophysical, and engineering work. As we shall see in the next chapter, these constitute the most dissatisfied sub-group of professional oilmen. Often they may be laid off, or may decide to leave the company or even the industry, although such professional drop-outs seem to be an exception.

Managerial Careers

In order to make it to the top in the corporate sector of the oil industry, young oilmen must opt for managerial careers by making the crucial shift from the technical to the administrative organizational ladder. The option to attempt this move is not, of course, entirely up to them; but those with managerial aspirations can let these be known and, if they are considered to have promise, will usually be given a chance to prove themselves. The lowest level of administrative job, as a leader of a project group, still involves a lot of technical work. This link helps ease the transition to the administrative ladder, where purely administrative and business concerns become proportionately more important as people move up. As they progress, their university and early training in the industry become more and more irrelevant. Except for a few in-house training courses, Canadian oilmen must learn their managerial and business skills on the job.[3]

The following is one man's account of his successful managerial career.

I took a general science degree in Manitoba. I was a kid from the farm. As far as aspirations were concerned when I was growing up, well I did well enough in school to keep on going to college. I just took the courses that came easiest. About the time I was ready to graduate I didn't have any firm ideas, although I had worked one summer in hard rock geology—enough to come to some understanding of geology. I found the natural sciences quite fascinating. An uncle of mine suggested that geophysics might be a good field, so I went to Toronto for a year of graduate school. Then I spent one summer in the seismic business in Alberta.

Actually, how I was drafted into Imperial, my uncle was working for Imperial at the time; I would have to say that he influenced me. I should have looked at other offers. That was back in the early fifties. Our training program at that time involved a moderate amount of time on a seismic crew, six weeks in my case; and then I had a six-week formal lecture-workshop type of course. Then I went to the Regina district as a trainee for a year or so. At that time we were putting interpreters back on geophysical crews; and I was on a crew for about a year and a half, and wandered around: Saskatchewan, Fort Macleod, Red Deer, Calgary, Fort St. John. That was probably a low point in my career.

Then I went to the Edmonton office as a junior interpreter. At that time I think I took a real serious responsibility for doing what was assigned to me as well as I possibly could, and perhaps a little more broadly than I thought. I was fairly competitive. Then we had a bit of an internal reorganization within the Edmonton division and went to an area system—four areas with a junior technical man assigned to each. I didn't immediately get an assignment like that and it bothered me; I began to worry that obviously I'd been slotted and other people were going to get more responsibility. But then I got the responsibility for a specialized geophysical program. Then I got an assignment as an area geophysicist; I found that quite satisfying. Really, since then I've never had time to get concerned about whether I could take on more responsibility than what I already had.

I later had a transfer from that job as an area geophysicist to our research department. I reoriented myself into more academic approaches to things; I liked that role, it gave me a chance to prove that I could be a scientist I guess. After that I got into a straight staff job for about five years; I found it satisfying and exciting.

I moved to Toronto on the staff there, and then came back here as an area-exploration manager, and now I'm manager of all our exploration operations. When the job was offered to me, it never occurred to me to consider turning it down. Not that I expected it at that time or at any particular time, but it was the next logical step in the system. In a big corporation, there's no such thing as standing still on the main line. In the future, as far as the main-line path is concerned, that leads to Toronto. . . .

This man was a confident manager, and others in the department believed that his next move would indeed be to an executive position at the corporate head office in Toronto. The logic of a successful managerial career leads, as he points out, to a senior-executive position and eventually a seat on the board of directors.

This man's career vision, like that of most Canadian oilmen, is largely restricted to Canada. But there is also an international flavour to the industry which, although less pronounced in this country than in most oil-producing areas, nevertheless contributes significantly to the breadth of choice that oilmen enjoy. Many older Albertan oilmen spent a number of years with parent affiliates in South America and the Caribbean before returning to Alberta after the major discoveries in the 1950s. Nearly all Canadian oilmen in the majors go on training programs to the United States. And a notable minority of senior managers who have started out with the Canadian majors have moved up to senior managerial positions with their American parents, the most notable example being the former chief executive officer of Exxon.

There is also a new breed of young professionals and managers which has grown up in response to the sort of organizational changes discussed in the last chapter. These individuals consciously view their careers in international terms. They see themselves as employees, not of Imperial and Shell Canada, but of Exxon Corporation and the Royal Dutch/Shell group.

> I could see myself in, well, there's one job in the corporation, a guy in New York who works in producing-co-ordination which is sort of a world-wide co-ordinator job. He's an ex-Canadian and a real salty explorationist. I could see myself doing that job very easily and it would sort of complement my love of travel. I think it would be a waste of the company's time to leave me at this desk for the next twenty years, and I think if I saw that coming I'd probably ask them to do something about it. I'm not so sure that my career really belongs at Imperial. It's a little bit of a family-style organization, I think perhaps I'm part of the larger family. I guess I'm telling you that my advancement model would be within the larger corporation.

This man sees himself as shaping his career in international terms within an international company. However, it is evidence of the cohesion of the Calgary oil community that this type is the exception rather than the rule, although many Canadian oilmen do enjoy short-term overseas experience.[4]

Of course, not all competent managers can reach the top, either within the Canadian major or its parent multinational. Positions become scarcer and competition keener the further up the hierarchy one moves. Those who do not quite make it to the top are accommodated by various staff positions, with important but secondary corporate responsibilities. The "main line" is cleared for other promising upwardly mobile managers.

Oilmen refer to the career stage when one's maximum level in the organization has been reached as "peaking". This can be a disappointing and disillusioning experience.

One of the trends in industry is the use of younger people in managerial positions, so I'm at an age where I can't look forward to any kind of managerial position—perhaps, I don't know. I guess you could say that once you get to forty-five plus and haven't reached your goal, you're not going to achieve it. It's kind of a downhill slide from that time until retirement I guess. You know that you're over the hump anyway. I blame the company in part for this too, the company's attitude has changed. My goals were never reached within the company that I had set for myself, I had hoped that I might be able to get up into the directors. Successful managers seem to exude some kind of a confidence most people don't have. As far as ability is concerned . . . I don't know.

Personal ease in social intercourse seems to be necessary for managerial career success. This may be displayed in "off-duty" situations—for example, at meetings of professional associations or on the golf course—although few oilmen believe that one can make it to the top through such informal channels alone. Proven managerial and entrepreneurial ability is the main requisite. Another career contingency involves moral choice. Rising managers may have to take courses of action that they do not really believe in, as in the purge discussed above. I was told of an unusual case where a promising young manager, who had been prevented from transferring some engineers into a project which he felt would be beneficial to their professional development, resigned in protest and went into farming. Such personal rebellions are rare. As in most businesses, oil managers make moral compromises or, when need be, rationalize their behaviour as being in the best long-term interests of the company, themselves, or their families.

Some lower-level managers decide themselves that the stress, strain, hard work, and family disruptions that striving for the top require may simply not be worth it.

I've reached a position where there is very definitely a trade-off between the quality of the job that I do here and the quality of my family life. I'm at a point of choice where I think if I devote sufficient effort, I could probably get a number of advances; but I think that in order to maintain the quality of life that I would like to have I seriously question whether I'd want more advances. From my wife's point of view, there's very much of a difference between Calgary and Toronto, she is very much happier in Calgary. Almost all the good friends we've made over the years are here.

Senior managers in a number of companies confirmed that there is a trend within the industry among some young professionals towards resisting upward career mobility. However, instead of simply dismissing these less-ambitious employees as they would probably have done in the past, the companies have tried to accommodate the "mobility resistors" somewhat (as their numbers have increased) by keeping them on at junior levels. These employees also often exhibit what oilmen call "field reticence" (or reluctance to stay in the field) and this has been given as one of the reasons for centralizing operations in Calgary. More than ever before, the new breed of professional is resisting moves both to central Canada and to the frontier towns.

Within the Canadian oil industry, however, barriers to intracompany mobility, whether imposed by others or as a matter of personal choice, are compensated for by the presence of other career opportunities. Once they have gained their basic training in the majors, oilmen can and do leave to take up new careers as consultants, as senior members of small oil companies, or even as independent oilmen.

Careers in Small Companies

The structure of the Canadian oil industry, with its combination of majors, large independents, small oil companies, and consulting firms, opens up a great variety of job opportunities to trained professional oilmen. One of their most important career decisions concerns whether they should stay with a major company or leave for a new challenge, either with a smaller company or as a consultant. Although a few people leave one major to work for another, this is unusual. The general feeling is that there is little point in moving to more of the same kind of work in a similar organization.

Opinions vary as to the relative merits of large and small companies. Technical professionals in the former argue that only the majors and largest independents have the capital and resources to be involved in the most interesting and challenging exploration and engineering problems. And they enjoy the opportunity to work with other experts in their field. In one man's words: "I see this position as being where the action is." Corporate managers enjoy their economic power and the experience of being intimately involved in the big decisions that affect the country's future.

The majors, however, cannot provide challenging managerial jobs to all who seek them. Many leave because they feel frustrated and lost within the big organizations, and because their career opportunities there seem restricted and dull. Small companies complement and reinforce this pressure to leave. They are always on the look-out for well-trained geologists, geophysicists, and engineers. To compete with the greater job security and prestige enjoyed by employees of the majors, they offer higher salaries and such fringe benefits as memberships in the Petroleum Club and various recreational clubs in the city. The scope of activities associated with any formal position is greater in the small companies than in the majors, there is less competition among would-be executives, and the ladder to senior managerial positions is shorter. One oilman, who had had experience with companies of varying sizes, argued as follows:

> I was only the seventh employee when BP bought that other company. Four years later they had 150 employees in Canada and I left because, well, if there's one thing I can't stand it's company politics —guys empire building and intra-company employee fighting. In little companies like this one it's beautiful because you run the land department and you get that kind of experience; you run the crude oil, you negotiate and sign the crude-oil purchase contracts and the gas contracts. You get a little bit of everything, it's very good experience. I've now had experience in pretty well all facets of the oil business.

Experienced professionals who go to work with small oil companies become managers and, usually, equity owners. They work harder and take greater risks. The company may go bankrupt, or it may strike it lucky and make them a lot of money. Generally, they develop a much closer identification with their company than do the employees of the majors. Indeed, as we have seen, there is little distinction between the company and its entrepreneurial leaders. Their careers become bound up with the career of the company. As with the senior executives in the majors, oil becomes integral to these people's lives. Professionals who remain as workers with the majors, on the other hand, prefer their more regular hours and the greater autonomy in their personal lives that the more impersonal relationship to the company allows. Older employees often stay with their large companies, despite career peaking, because of the commitments they have built up in pension plans, longer annual holidays, and the prospect of early retirement.

The following account of a successful career with a small company is by a man who had worked for a large, international British company which was bought out by a major. He was then approached by the directors of a small Alberta company.

> That was in 1952. There was this little entity which had just been financed by a group of Bay Street financiers. We bought out some properties, and I was able to go back to my friends in ＿＿＿ whom I had left three or four years before, and I had by that time developed sufficient assets to ask them to invest in our company. They agreed, so I raised quite a bit of money on the basis of the reserves that we had managed to put into the group of companies, and from that point we were able to use that money to buy further assets and so on and we built up the company from that point.

This man is currently the chairman of the company, which is becoming a large Canadian independent. His case illustrates how a move to a small company represents a shift from an organizational to an entrepreneurial career (House, 1974: 110–24).[5] Career success becomes more a function of building up the enterprise as a whole than of moving up an organizational hierarchy. This applies as well to consultants' careers.

Careers as Consultants

Consulting offers similar opportunities for individual entrepreneurship and autonomy and entails the same sort of risk-taking found in small companies. Indeed, many individuals' oil careers involve working both in small companies and as consultants. Consulting provides a basic income while they try to find the capital and opportunity to establish their own companies. Oilmen may leave the majors at any point in their careers to enter consulting, but three main patterns can be distinguished.

Some oilmen leave early in their careers, just when they have become expert petroleum engineers or geologists. People choosing this option continue to do the same type of work but on a contract basis with numerous different companies. This gives them greater freedom and autonomy in that they can work more or less when they like and take longer holidays. In expansionary phases of the industry they do well financially, but they are vulnerable to economic recessions. To gain a measure of security, they often associate themselves with larger consulting firms on a sub-contract or fee basis. In general, they do not expect to get wealthy as consultants, but prefer autonomy to the security of working full-time for an oil company. They often attempt to further their careers by informal public-relations efforts.

> I'm involved with PR. I make sure I get my picture in the paper, and the *Roughneck* [an oilman's periodical]. People see my name coming up every three or four months. A lot of guys don't do this, but it makes it easier if you do come up. You contact somebody and they say: "Oh, I've heard that name before." And I got myself in the news with the ski club. You make contacts through skiing with other geologists. For example, I got my contracts with _____ because the guy I contacted was in the club.

This strategy, however, can be overplayed if one gives the impression that one's friendships are feigned for business purposes.

The second type of move into consulting seems to be made by oilmen who have reached their career peaks within a large oil company, either as a high-level technical expert or as a middle-level manager. People in the former category can become technical consultants; they are in high demand from smaller oil companies, and even from the large independents and majors for certain specialized problems. Technical experts may work on their own, but this means that they must start to develop business skills in which they may have had no previous training or practice. Many prefer to join the larger consulting firms in which the senior people find themselves becoming organizational managers in their own right.

The third type of move is made by those who have advanced into senior managerial positions with the large companies. Late in their careers, sometimes even after formal retirement, they decide to become consultants, offering business expertise and deal-making ability to interested clients.[6] A man who grew up with the industry in Alberta while working his way up to a high-level position in a major, left to work overseas, and then returned to Alberta as a consultant gives this account:

> I have an academic background in geology, and my connection in exploration dates as far back as 1934 here in Alberta. That was the first decade in the application of the technology of the earth sciences. In that period of time I sort of lived and worked along the foothills and in the Arctic. After that period and for the next ten years I worked in the head office of the company in Toronto. I did some short-term assignments for the parent company, in Cuba before Castro, in Venezuela. And I worked in resource research in short-term assignments in Tulsa and Houston and New York. So I drifted around a little bit in this hemisphere. Then, after Leduc, I came back to Calgary as general manager for the company for all of western Canada, and I was on the board. This was in the fifties and early sixties. Then in the middle sixties I left the company and I went overseas and I worked the eastern hemisphere, Sydney, Australia, for a little while, and from there I went to London, England, and was involved in the North Sea and the Mediterranean and Europe.
>
> When I came back here, I went into consulting. Now I'm walking the other side of the street, I'm an independent consultant. Essentially, I'm giving advice to independent companies. And I'm a director in _____ [a medium-sized Canadian independent with interests in the North Sea].

This man's career demonstrates nicely the point that professionals in the Canadian oil industry enjoy the "luxury of choice". Partly because availability of varied opportunities is built in to the industry's structure and partly because of his own decisions at various points in his professional life, his career has included phases as a technical professional in Canada, the United States, and South America; as a senior manager and director in a Canadian major; as a manager with various affiliates of multinationals and smaller companies in Australia and Europe; as an independent consultant selling the knowledge and expertise gained through his multi-faceted experience; and as a director of a rapidly growing Canadian independent intimately involved in the international oil business. His career epitomizes what it means to be a successful

Canadian oilman. It contrasts sharply to the more limited opportunities open to most non-professionals in the industry.

Non-professional Careers

Professional university training is, by and large, a necessary prerequisite for a high-ranking career in the oil industry. Non-professionals enjoy far fewer opportunities than professionals and face almost insurmountable odds in trying to make it to the top, particularly in the major companies. We have already seen that there is a sharp formal organizational distinction between rural-based field operations and urban-based office operations. The most that a non-professional working on-site at a producing oil field can aspire to is the position of field supervisor or, in some cases, area supervisor of a number of adjacent fields. In Alberta, where many of the men who hold these positions felt fortunate to get a job at all after the last war, there appears to be little resentment about this barrier to career mobility. Within the Calgary office, a similar combination of career immobility and lack of class consciousness and resentment is found among the female clerical and secretarial staff.

Within the exploration and production department at Imperial, professional engineers and explorationists have started to resist working for extended periods in the field. The company has responded by creating a new category of worker, the "technologist". This is a kind of intermediary status between non-professional technicians on the one hand, and professional engineers, geologists, and geophysicists on the other. Technologists are trained at the Northern and the Southern Alberta Institutes of Technology (NAIT and SAIT), which are located in Edmonton and Calgary, respectively. Increasingly, they are being used to do the kind of technical and supervisory work that geologists and engineers used to do at well-sites and in field-production operations. Technologists are also used as technical assistants to professional workers within the Calgary office. Unlike the non-professional field workers who lack formal training, many technologists have come to resent their position. They feel as competent as many professionals, but face rigid barriers to moving into management, or even on to the higher rungs of the technical ladder.

> There's a problem in that they won't really have a technologist going to a district to replace a geologist. Imperial has a very rigid system. I'm not making any bones about it, I think the technologist is a graduate too, so your work is going to be on the same level. But they just don't have the areas for the technologists to go into. This is a real problem in our company—what to do with the technologists.

A few technologists have been rewarded for outstanding technical achievement by being moved to the higher rungs of the technical ladder, which are referred to, significantly, as the "professional ladder". In the early days of the industry, some individuals learned to become competent petroleum geologists and engineers through on-the-job training, and later moved into management, but this mobility pattern is no longer found.

Within the majors, the best opportunities for non-professionals lie in departments related to but distinct from exploration and production as such. These include land and contracts, and scouting for information, both areas in which job qualifications have not become as formalized and professionalized as they are in most other oil-industry activities. The land and contracts department (separate departments in some companies) execute and administer the company's land position and handle a great variety of contracts with other companies, government agencies, and individual land-owners upon whose property wells are drilled or pipelines laid. Junior members of such departments spend much of their time in the field negotiating with farmers and other landlords. As their careers progress, they can move up into managerial positions with a great deal of responsibility and make an important entrepreneurial input into the company's operations. These land-men are the internal deal-makers within the majors. Their mobility barrier is at the middle-management level, as they have little chance of advancing to head-office positions. As we have seen (pp. 81-85), scouting was one of the more romantic aspects of the industry during the heyday of exploration in the western provinces. However, it has gradually evolved into a sophisticated system of information procurement, storage, and retrieval both within the company and within the industry more generally. Modern "scouts" have become computer experts and systems theorists; still, as long as these skills can be acquired through internal training programs, the need for them continues to provide career opportunities to non-professionals.

The best opportunities for non-professionals to "make it" in a big way in the contemporary oil scene, however, lie outside the major companies, where they are free to compete as specu-lators, deal-makers, and entrepreneurs in small companies. In the Texas oil boom, and in the early period of growth in southern Alberta, many individuals founded family fortunes through acquiring freehold rights to oil and gas and collecting large royalties as their wells went into production. This oppor-tunity was removed in most of the later development in central and northern Alberta, Saskatchewan, British Columbia, and the northern and offshore frontiers, as governments passed legislation reserving all mineral rights to the Crown. Further-more, as land positions have become consolidated in all of the promising areas of Canada, land speculation is less promising as a means to a quick fortune. Some individuals do, however, continue to strike it rich through putting together successful exploration plays in small companies, or by buying marginal producing properties which they can operate less expensively than can the majors; and many of these are people who have had no formal professional training. Previous business experi-ence is, however, important, as the following account suggests:

> I was in the insurance business and in the investment business. That assisted me in the oil business because the oil industry is no different than any other business. It's a sales business, it's a busi-ness where you deal with people. I had been instrumental in merg-ing three companies, not oil companies, but the finder's fee repre-sented a cash asset, and I was able to raise some funds on an equity basis to go into the oil industry. I bought a little oil field, not knowing anything about the business, but I had an engineer look at things and I went around to see various oil companies. There were two majors or large independents and they agreed to sell me the property. It was a marginal property for a major, they weren't making any money out of it but I could operate it much more inexpensively. They had to pay a superintendent to oversee it, they had to pay a pumper and their expenses were far higher than mine. At the time the price of oil was very low. This was heavy oil and the price was $1.88 a barrel. It's now about $6.00 a barrel. . . .

Such individual entrepreneurs, whether professionals or non-professionals, can continue to make it in the Canadian oil industry because they can contribute non-marketable resources such as their own time and cheaper labour through business connections to compete with the majors in marginal drilling prospects and producing properties (Krohn, Fleming, and Manzer, 1977).

CONCLUSION

The western-Canadian oil industry is structured in such a way that it provides a great variety of career opportunities to its members, particularly those with formal training in engineering, geology, and geophysics. Typically, professionals start their careers as workers with major oil companies. But, depending upon their early success, the growth of the industry itself, and their own preferences and choices, a great variety of career possibilities may open out to them. If they continue as professional workers, they can do so as well-paid organization men in the majors or large independents, or they can become technical-specialist consultants working on their own or on a contract or fee basis with a consulting firm. As another alternative, they can pursue an organizational career as a manager within a large company, where success depends upon moving up the organization's hierarchy of formal offices. Or, as yet another alternative, they can leave the majors to pursue entrepreneurial careers as deal-making consultants or as members of small oil companies. Career failure, on the other hand, is found among those who stagnate at low-level technical jobs, peak out at low managerial levels, and run into personal or market-induced difficulties as consultants or small businessmen.

Non-professional workers, particularly field workers and secretaries and the semi-professional technologists, face insurmountable career barriers within the major companies, although a few non-professionals can make it to middle-level managerial levels in the land-and-contracts department and in scouting. Outside the majors, some non-professionals, particularly those with business experience, can pursue successful entrepreneurial careers.

Although our main focus has been upon the way in which career opportunities are structured by industry organization, it should be noted that career contingencies also feed back upon the industry's organization. To compete with the smaller companies, the majors and large independents have had to provide

higher salaries and greater working autonomy to their professional workers than they might otherwise have done. The position of technologist was invented to compensate for the increased resistance among professionals to field-work assignments. And the fact that many technical and business experts
choose careers as consultants has created the opportunity for
both the majors and the small companies to do much of their
work on a contract basis.

In other words, the breadth of career choice available to
oilmen is a logical corollary to the flexibility that seems to be
inherent in the Canadian oil industry. This combination of
flexible structure and numerous and varied career opportunities is responsible for the high level of job satisfaction within
the industry.

CHAPTER SIX

The Structuring of Job Satisfaction

Sociologists tend to eschew explanations in terms of differences in personal abilities, choices, and decisions. Yet, to avoid a misleading, mechanistic, and static view of social life, it has to be recognized that the active, creative side of human nature must be taken into account, both in a collective and an individual sense (Marx, 1887; Mead, 1934). In the last chapter, we saw on the one hand how the organization of the oil industry structures career opportunities; and, on the other, how personal career choices, in turn, feed back upon the way in which the industry is organized.

This flexible organization and career variety, in turn, structure job satisfaction within the oil industry, in the sense that they provide a striking context of choice which accommodates individual differences of talent, interest, and ambition. Most professional oilmen manage to find industry niches that suit them, and this largely accounts for the high level of job satisfaction and low level of subjective alienation within the industry. Only those few who fail to find such niches become dissatisfied and alienated.

This chapter examines two kinds of evidence about job satisfaction. First, it uses quantitative data from the survey of oilmen to show that over-all job satisfaction is indeed strikingly high and alienation low; and, through multivariate analysis, explores some of the working conditions and organizational features associated with various levels of satisfaction and alienation. This kind of analysis will give an initial understanding of the underlying processes that account for the findings and associations. In the second part of the chapter, these processes are further explored and illustrated using the more impressionistic information obtained from personal interviews. Whereas the quantitative data provide important hard facts about job satisfaction and its correlates, the interview data explain the underlying context and causes that give meaning to the objective data.[1]

CALGARY OILMEN AS SATISFIED WORKERS[2]

Despite their sometimes sophisticated appearance, quantitative techniques for measuring subjective states of human populations should be viewed as rough instruments. This proviso notwithstanding, our survey does provide striking evidence that Calgary oilmen are highly satisfied with their jobs and are, as a rule, not alienated in their work. This is clearly indicated in figures 6:1 and 6:2 which show high scores for over-all job satisfaction and low scores for alienation.[3] (Readers unfamiliar with quantitative variable analysis might prefer to skim to the next section.) The fact that 88 per cent of the oilmen sampled scored above the median scale value on the scale for satisfaction and 98 per cent below the median scale value for aliena-

FIGURE 6:1   Job Satisfaction (Over-all) of Sample of Calgary Oilmen

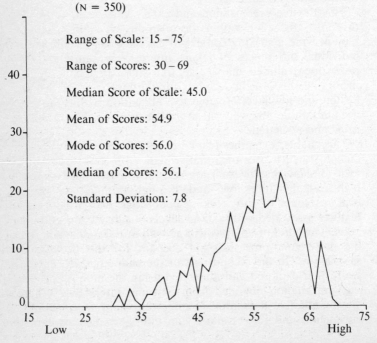

(N = 350)

Range of Scale: 15 – 75

Range of Scores: 30 – 69

Median Score of Scale: 45.0

Mean of Scores: 54.9

Mode of Scores: 56.0

Median of Scores: 56.1

Standard Deviation: 7.8

FIGURE 6:2　Subjective Alienation (Over-all) of Sample of Calgary Oilmen (N = 349)

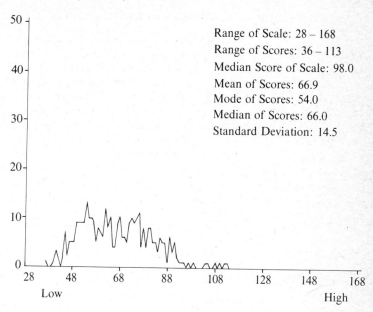

Range of Scale: 28 – 168
Range of Scores: 36 – 113
Median Score of Scale: 98.0
Mean of Scores: 66.9
Mode of Scores: 54.0
Median of Scores: 66.0
Standard Deviation: 14.5

tion is convincing. Whereas only 2 per cent of oilmen scored above the scale median on alienation, an earlier study found scores ranging from 19 to 93 per cent on the various alienation sub-scales for three groups of blue-collar workers (Shepard, 1973: 75). The data from personal interviews are consistent with and thereby lend validity to this claim. The findings also appear to be reliable, as they are consistent for the various sub-scales. Job-satisfaction frequency distributions are skewed towards the high ends of the scales for pay, recognition and accomplishment, advancement, commitment, and relations with co-workers and supervisor; while alienation scores are skewed towards the low ends of the scales for powerlessness, meaninglessness, instrumental work orientation, self-evaluative work involvement, and isolation from the goals of the industry. The powerlessness and meaninglessness scales are particularly striking for their low scores.

Although the survey data preclude our getting at the underlying reasons for the above findings, we were able to discover important leads by establishing the organizational and work correlates of job satisfaction and alienation. In investigating these, we used a variety of statistical procedures for exploring the data along the lines suggested by Glaser and Strauss (1967) rather than the more usual hypothesis-testing format familiar to sociologists. Although a few variables, such as organizational level, appeared to be related to satisfaction and alienation in simple cross-tabulations, these relationships proved to be weak when controlled for other variables. Indeed, the data are striking for the variables that are *not* significantly correlated with job satisfaction and alienation. These include: occupation, intra-company mobility, inter-company mobility, age, years working in the industry, years with present company, and education.

In manipulating the data further, a number of exploratory statistical procedures were used (correlations, analysis of variance, multiple-classification analysis, factor analysis) to arrive at a list of variables which consistently appeared to be important. A step-by-step regression analysis was then run with these variables.[4] (The findings for the regression analysis are summarized in Appendix II, Tables II: 10 and II:11.) The most important variable in explaining both job satisfaction and alienation is *achievement opportunity*. This variable refers to one's perceived opportunity to involve oneself in and to complete challenging and interesting pieces of work. It is not achievement in the sense of upward mobility. The questions which comprised this scale (modified from Patchen, 1970: 98, 75, 77) were as follows:

In connection with your job, how much chance do you get:
a) to do the kinds of things you're best at?
b) to show your full potential?
c) to learn new things?
d) to see your projects or assignments fully completed?

The nature of the work itself, then, appears to be the key variable in explaining high job satisfaction and low subjective alienation. Oilmen who answered "a good chance" or "an excellent chance" to the above questions enjoyed their work and felt fulfilled in it; and the oil industry in Calgary provides this kind of opportunity to most of its entrepreneurs, managers, and professional workers.[5]

The overwhelming importance of the nature of the work itself in determining job satisfaction is further shown by the second and third variables from the step-by-step regression analysis for job satisfaction. These were job involvement and job participation. People who feel deeply involved in their jobs, and who feel that they themselves participate in scheduling their own work and deciding how their tasks are to be done, tend to be highly satisfied. The fourth variable, job codification, appears to be something of an anomaly, as one would not expect that those whose jobs are more strictly codified would be more satisfied. Note, however, that the simple "r" for this variable is extremely low (0.006) and it adds little to the amount of variance explained.

Turning to the other variables related to alienation, job involvement again shows up, as well as three other variables. The most important new variable is participation in decison-making. Those who score high on decision-making score low on alienation. This suggests that, in addition to the nature of the work itself, one's actual participation in decisions about the organization and about other employees affects one's subjective alienation, but not one's job satisfaction. Alienation is also related to job codification. The more formalized one's working conditions, the more alienated one feels. Finally, surprisingly, income shows up as being positively correlated with alienation ($r = 0.38$), although it adds little to the additional variance explained. Possibly those with high incomes but low achievement opportunity and job involvement feel alienated by their incongruous position compared to lower-earning colleagues with similar working conditions.

These quantitative data are highly suggestive for understanding the proximate causes of the high level of job satisfaction reported by most Calgary oilmen. They are supported in greater depth, and rounded out in terms of the larger structural context which has been our main focus, by the data collected from personal interviews.

THE VARIETIES OF JOB SATISFACTION

Interviewees were asked conversational, open-ended questions about job satisfaction, such as: "How do you enjoy your work?" "What do you like about it?"[6] "What do you dislike about it?" Their responses confirmed both impressions gained from the survey; most oilmen expressed high job satisfaction, and most cited the interesting nature of the work itself and their freedom to decide how to perform their own tasks as the main reasons for that satisfaction. The following comments, the first by an engineer and the second by a geologist, illustrate this finding:

> I find it really challenging and satisfying to have the freedom to go ahead and organize this thing. The problems involved are really fundamental. So here's an example of a sort of task, a self-created job you might say. So there's great satisfaction in that.

> I'm certainly getting job satisfaction. It's not the money; I could live quite comfortably on quite a lot less than I'm getting. I feel I have enough autonomy. It's not making decisions really, but we make recommendations to management. The more I'm getting into the job, the more autonomy I'm getting. It's not a rigid thing; there's no line that says "thou shalt not make a decision". We're just making more and more decisions, bigger and bigger recommendations, so there's no real constraint. If you feel that you need something, it doesn't matter what it is, or if you have to talk to somebody or visit somebody or get some engineering work done, the co-operation is there.

The interview data also give another insight into the reasons for job satisfaction within the industry that the quantitative survey did not reveal. This is the great variety of sources of satisfaction that different individuals find in different jobs. They run the whole gamut of positions within the industry.

> *Production Engineer.* I think I've been more fortunate than most in the respect that I haven't had to do much psyching of myself. I've always been involved in jobs that I think, from an objective point of view, would be considered to be relevant and challenging. Oh, there've been some lulls, I guess there are lulls in everybody's career, but by and large I've been very happy in my work.

> *Research Engineer.* It's interesting work, challenging. I think what makes it even more exciting is that you're on the very forefront of technology.

> *Geologist.* There's never a dull moment. One of the nice things is that it's not as much routine as you'd think, 'cause every morning something else will happen. And one of the interesting things is

you're on top of our current activity, knowing exactly what's happening in your part of the world.

Geophysicist. I think the over-all interest in drilling wells, well, it's like canoeing down a river; you don't know what's around the next bend. It's quite a thrill being part of an organization that can find a 500-million-barrel oil field or a major gas field.

Junior Manager. There's no question, I couldn't do some of the technical jobs. But a lot of our input is seeing the economic climate, seeing where the opportunities are going to lie, and making sure we have people that are already working on the problem at the right time. That's the real challenge because that's the innovative challenge. It's fascinating, fascinating. You've got all these experts, so from the mental point of view it's enormously stimulating.

Senior Manager. I don't have any frustration whatsoever; I feel that I haven't been inhibited from making decisions that I thought were important simply because I had to go through some prearranged formal ritual. I think it's one of the best jobs in the country; it's involved in a business that's critical. I feel myself part of the team responsible for one of the most important industries in Canada.

Staff position. For the last five or six years my work has been just fantastic. I've become involved in almost entirely environmental work in an advisory position, and it's taken me all over the continent. And I've been invited to speak on transportation at the Arctic summer school; it's been very satisfying.

Manager, Small Company. The thing I like about working for an independent or small company is that you're part of the decision-making and anything that happens you know about. It's part of your life, and everything that happens directly affects you. I find that really is the best part of working in the business.

Manager, Drilling Company. The satisfaction is that you can build it up. . . . It's a very competitive business; you feel that you can do something, drill a better well or a faster well or you can make more money or whatever it is.

Manager, Service Company. Every morning even now, I'm happy to come to work; I look forward to it. I think it's because this business is, well, you never know when you come in here in the morning what's going to be asked of you. It could be different every day; generally it is.

Consultant. Well, personally, I really can't say anything nasty about the oil industry. It has been exceptionally good to me; I've enjoyed every minute of it; I enjoy the people who are in it; I would never leave it.

Underlying this high level of job satisfaction is the breadth of career choice that oilmen enjoy. They assess alternative career routes in the light of their own interests and, to a large extent, can choose the path that gives greatest satisfaction. For some people, however, there are structurally imposed limits upon career choice and job satisfaction.

THE SOURCES OF JOB DISSATISFACTION

Most oilmen, even the highly satisfied, do find certain aspects of their work and careers boring and unfulfilling. Within the large companies, in particular, a fair amount of paper work is required of professional workers and managers—filling in forms, completing reports on oneself and others, writing letters, answering memos. Most find this work dull and frustrating, particularly the junior- and middle-level managers who do the greatest share of it.

Oilmen at all levels and within all types of companies also feel unhappy about the industry's poor public image. They believe in the value of their work and in their contribution to the Canadian economy and society, but feel that this contribution is unappreciated and misunderstood by governments and the public.

The main dissatisfaction for me is the poor public image we have. We give people good jobs, we work on the environment, we contribute a lot to this country—we work hard for it. But we just don't have that image. It makes me mad sometimes. Just compare us to the civil servants, try getting something out of them on a weekend. Well, we can't get away with that, we just have to get our work done.

Another much cited source of dissatisfaction, particularly in the big companies, is the communications problem, and the conflict arising from it, that seems to plague line-staff relations (cf. Dalton, 1959). The source of this problem is usually structural and occurs when employees who lack authority over other employees are dependent upon them for certain tasks and services which may not be provided when needed. The frustration is particularly galling for those in staff positions who feel left out of the industry's main activities.

> There's lots of frustrations to a staff assignment. I was always one that liked to be doing things, getting things done, working that old drilling schedule up. I don't get involved in that anymore; I have to force myself to stay out of somebody else's responsibility. Often you see things done less efficiently than you used to do them, but they don't like you bitching about other people's work. I'm used on a consulting basis, and this frustrates me because I'm getting bits and pieces. I'm not lining up how things should be done, really, because people are not working for me.

Within the production department of Imperial Oil, this kind of frustration from internal conflict is also found between field-operations and central-engineering staff. Usually, the conflict is expressed in personal terms as between experienced field operators and more theoretically trained engineers, but the conflict also reflects an organizational split between staff and line functions.

All of the above sources of dissatisfaction are found among people who, for the most part, enjoy their jobs. But there are two groups of oilmen, within the majors at least, who find their work more generally dissatisfying. The first are those whose careers have peaked and who find themselves suffering from the agonies caused by career reversal and its attendant loss of status. The following comment is by a man who was demoted from the managerial to the technical career ladder.

> I think, in supervisory work, it can get to be a real gut breaker; you've got to come to grips with having to fire a guy, so it makes more demands in certain respects. But I enjoyed it; it was probably the height of my working career with the company. When I came back to technical work, it was a letdown. It's frustrating because I came from supervisory operations into gas. My main occupation now is compressors—I'd never even seen one! It's a pretty traumatic experience. You go out and you know nothing. What the hell should you be doing? To me this is really poor handling of a guy's career. I don't know what else you can do, maybe just quit. But you don't quit unless you're really unhappy. I'm not saying I'm unhappy, just let down.

Even though one may still have technically challenging work, the relative deprivation after demotion does cause dissatisfaction.

The second type of basic dissatisfaction is more serious, because it has to do with the nature of the work itself. Some exploration and engineering tasks are inherently boring and routine, particularly after a person has been doing them for some time. To an extent, the company deals with this problem by allocating such tasks to beginners, and reduces the monotony by circulating people among the tasks. But this strategy can work to only a limited extent. The other type of solution is to leave professional workers who are not considered to have great promise in such work for long periods. These people constitute the most alienated and dissatisfied of oilmen.[7]

> In four years I really haven't had any demanding jobs. It's almost like being a technican. I've talked to guys who feel the same way. You're not using the technical ability you're trained for. You're pushing pencils, pushing paper, pushing numbers. Pretty well all the time I've been a reservoir engineer. That's my major complaint; I'd like to try something else. My main complaint with ____ [her group leader] is that we aren't allowed to make suggestions or if we do suggest something, it appears weeks later as someone else's idea. You pick up one of these simulations I'm doing now and you're doing it, it seems like the rest of your life. Two years later you look back and say, my God I'm still doing the same thing. I'd like to go to the Cold Lake group, it's more interesting work, or something new, the frontier, research. If that doesn't work out, then I'll quit and go to a small company. You get lost in a major company; you feel like a number after a while. You could have a Grade 12 education and do most of the things I'm doing here.

As these comments show, the causes of dissatisfaction for this minority of oil-industry employees are the opposite of the causes of satisfaction for most. The stereotypical, alienative reference to working for a big company is, I think, more a projection of this woman's dissatisfaction than a general observation about work in the majors. If she were promoted to more interesting and challenging work on the Cold Lake project or in a frontier area, she would feel more like a person and less like a number. The relationship between organizational structure, job satisfaction, and alienation is more complex than our static survey analysis suggests.

ORGANIZATIONAL STRUCTURE, ALIENATION, AND JOB
SATISFACTION

As we have seen, and as common sense suggests, there is a
fairly high negative correlation between job satisfaction and
alienation for Calgary oilmen (r = -0.47). In general, people
who feel left out of the decision-making process and who lack
control over their own working conditions are unhappy in their
work. The correlation, however, is far from perfect; and, indeed, the correlation between over-all satisfaction and the instrumental work-orientation sub-scale is only r = -0.22. This
suggests that the relationship between subjective alienation
and job satisfaction is less than perfect empirically and, more
profoundly, that the philosophical notion of alienation involves
a projection of some people's ideas about favourable working
conditions upon others. Some individuals feel uncomfortable
about the responsibilities and stresses of making decisions, particularly about people and large organizational goals and expenditures.[8] For such people, the *sine qua non* of job satisfaction is that they find work that is inherently satisfying, and that
they be given the autonomy to get on with the job. Professionals in organizations, such as doctors on hospital staffs and
professors in universities, as well as professional athletes, art-
ists, and actors and actresses, are obvious examples. To many
of them, indeed, administrative decision-making is a boring
and less prestigious task to be left to those without the talent to
make it as surgeons, academics, and so forth.

The concern for worker partcipation in management, and
democratization of the organization of work, we might hypoth-
esize, comes more from those workers who perform boring,
unfulfilling jobs than from those with inherently interesting
tasks. The professional oil workers we interviewed not only
accepted the oligarchical decision-making process as legitimate,
but had hardly considered the possibility of its being any different. When asked specifically about worker participation,
they had great difficulty in even understanding the question;
and, when it was explained, dismissed it summarily: "Oh, that
sort of thing would never work here. You need qualified people
in the top positions."

This background discussion helps explain why some professional workers in the oil industry would show up in the survey
as both fairly highly alienated and highly satisfied. There is no
contradiction in suggesting that they found their work satisfy-

ing and fulfilling yet did not feel as though they had much say in organizational decision-making and did not consider their work to be the most important part of their life.[9] Again, the interview data are richer for exploring the complexity of the relationships among organizational form, alienation, and job satisfaction.

> It's really interesting, I like the work. I've often asked myself: "Am I right going into engineering?" You can get pretty disillusioned with the setup in a big corporation; you're a little cog in the wheel. But one thing I like about the company is that, once your sights are set, the opportunity's there, the door is open. You can't just walk right through it, you have to hassle a bit and work and struggle. I think as long as you show initiative and work hard there's every opportunity in a big company. I've certainly enjoyed it; it's rewarding. You see I'm one of these people, work to me is a professional capacity, I don't live for it. I use my work, I've got to be interested in it to a point where I can stand a full eight-hour day, five days a week, and find some reward in it. But then my real living comes in all kinds of interests outside of work.

This man was, we might suggest, ambiguously, and with qualifications, both alienated and satisfied, and his comments soften the meaning of both these terms for his case. As a survey respondent, he would misleadingly have appeared as unambiguously alienated and satisfied without qualifications, and these would have seemed like hard-and-fast psychological traits.

It is perhaps more accurate to say that the impersonality of a big organization is not inherently alienating but a source of dissatisfaction to some. Again, the analogy to small-town/big-city differences applies. Some prefer the increased intimacy of the former, some the greater variety of opportunities of the latter. Most people are, to varying degrees, ambivalent. The following comments are by a man who made the unusual career move from a small consulting firm to a demanding technical position with a major oil company.

> I'm certainly getting job satisfaction now, and the more I'm getting into the job the more autonomy I'm getting. The ability to get other expertise is part of it. We have a comparatively free hand to get things done. When I was with a consulting company I was a senior guy and I ran my own show, had a group of people working for

me, wrote my own proposals, cost control, this sort of stuff. Here, you're just a number, there's no doubt about it. You're just a number in a big organization. Top management don't even know me; whereas before I was a very good friend of the person who owned the business. But, oh, it's different; the satisfactions are a little different, it takes a while to adjust. I'm not sure which I like best, I certainly enjoy both.

CONCLUSION

Perhaps the key argument of this chapter is summarized in a phrase from the last quote where, in comparing his experiences in two types of organizations, the oilman concluded, "Oh, it's different, the satisfactions are a little different." Granted that some over-all assessment of job satisfaction level within an industry or occupation seems feasible, the attempt to delineate the dimensions of satisfaction and to compare respondents along the *same* dimensions may be misplaced. We may be trying to measure what cannot really be measured, since different jobs in different organizational settings produce a variety of satisfactions and dissatisfactions for different types of people. The attempt to render the philosophical idea of alienation into an objective, scientific concept is even more questionable, as it unwittingly builds values about democratic decision-making, scope for individuality, and the supreme worthiness of work into an ostensibly value-free "variable".[10]

Despite these limitations, our quantitative survey data have established that most Calgary oilmen are, indeed, very satisfied with their work; and this satisfaction is highly correlated with work-related variables, particularly opportunities for achievement in one's immediate tasks. The more complex interview data illustrate and confirm both these findings. More broadly, they suggest that job satisfaction is essentially a function of finding work that is interesting and challenging. The oil industry in Calgary provides a great variety of such jobs to professionally trained people. From this perspective, careers are the processes whereby people sort themselves out into those jobs best suited to their interests, talents, and aspirations. Not all jobs, however, are satisfying, and not all careers are successful. Career failure, either in the initial stage or later after one's career has peaked and declined, is associated with job dissatisfaction and a feeling of alienation. Alienation, in this personal, qualitative sense, is not so much a product of a particular organizational form as it is the subjective concomitant of being stuck with the duller jobs within an exciting industry. On the whole, the internal organization of the capitalist oil industry in Alberta is striking for the high level of job satisfaction it provides for most of its professional employees.

CHAPTER SEVEN

Beliefs: The Oil Community in Crisis

Whatever the objective facts of the situation may have been, there is no doubt that the Calgary oil community considered itself to be deeply threatened by the events of 1973 and 1974, when the OPEC countries took control of their oil and raised its price dramatically, and governments in Canada, both provincial and federal, began to assert more control over the industry.[1] To understand the oilmen's perceptions of events and the depth of their feelings, it is necessary to place these in the perspective of a world-view that is long-established among oil-industry personnel. By world-view I mean a loosely organized (and sometimes contradictory) set of ideas and concepts which shape the oilman's view of his social world and his interpretation of events within that world. I have termed their world-view the "myth of free enterprise" because its core ideas—translated into the terms of the popular consciousness—are derived from the writings of Adam Smith and the nineteenth-century British political economists and supplemented by a few provisos that allow for the peculiar nature of the North American oil industry in the twentieth century. I will, eventually, compare this world-view critically to the reality it purports to represent. But first the view itself and, in particular, the tenacity and conviction with which it is held by most oilmen should be discussed. It is a view that has been thoroughly internalized by many oilmen, so that the threat posed by the events of the early 1970s was seen by many of them as a threat not just to their material well-being but also to their personal identities. The oilmen experienced this as a time when their way of life seemed jeopardized by forces beyond their control not just at the international, but also at the national and the provincial levels.

CONSERVATISM: ECONOMIC, POLITICAL, AND RELIGIOUS

It will surprise no one to learn that Canadian oilmen are conservative in their economic thinking and political allegiances. Even so, the unanimity of their views and the depth of feeling with which they are held are striking. Figure 7:1 summarizes the results for our survey on the Minnesota economic conservatism scale. This evidence of conservatism is confirmed in personal interviews where, with monotonous regularity, oilmen uphold the rights of private property, of profits, of fair returns on investments, of the efficiency of the free-enterprise system; and oppose increased government involvement, the welfare state, and militant unionism. At the political level, these beliefs lead to a preference for the Progressive Conservative party (Table 7:1). It should be noted, however, that many oilmen feel that no current political party fairly represents their views and interests—they are all too "socialistic".

Our survey tapped one other source of information about oilmen's beliefs—their religious preferences. This is summarized in Table 7:2, which suggests that many oilmen are practising protestants. Several interviewees cited voluntary mem-

FIGURE 7:1   Economic Conservatism of Sample of Calgary Oilmen
(N = 350)

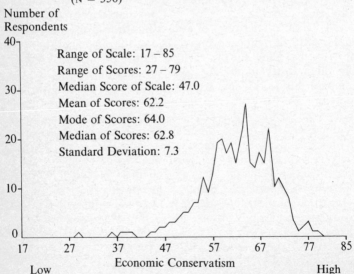

Range of Scale: 17 – 85
Range of Scores: 27 – 79
Median Score of Scale: 47.0
Mean of Scores: 62.2
Mode of Scores: 64.0
Median of Scores: 62.8
Standard Deviation: 7.3

TABLE 7:1 Political-Party Preferences of Sample of Calgary Oilmen

| | FEDERAL | | PROVINCIAL | |
	Number	Per cent	Number	Per cent
Conservative	246	75.7	249	78.8
Liberal	69	21.2	5	1.6
Social Credit	7	2.2	56	17.7
NDP	2	0.6	5	1.6
Other	1	0.3	1	0.3
Totals	325		316	

TABLE 7:2 Religious Preferences of Samples of Calgary Oilmen and Calgary Academics (Percentages)

	ACADEMIC	OILMEN
No Preference	41.9	20.7
Roman Catholic	8.8	17.2
United Church	11.5	37.0
Anglican	12.8	14.6
Jewish	2.7	—
Other	19.6	9.3
	N = 148	N = 343

bership on church committees as their main form of community involvement. These findings suggest that Max Weber's thesis about the relationship between protestantism and capitalism continues to have relevance in Canada today (Weber, 1930). Certainly, oilmen are more homogeneous in their beliefs and more religious than the members of another occupational group—Calgary academics—to whom the question was also administered (Table 7:2).

THE DEPTH OF BELIEFS

The survey data clearly confirm that oilmen are economically and politically conservative, but they fail to say much about the qualitative aspects of their thinking or about the depth of feeling with which their beliefs are held. One of the most striking findings of the survey, however, was the extent to which respondents felt called upon to add additional comments about their political and economic views on the economic-conservatism-scale questions, on the question about political allegiance, or in the space at the end where respondents were invited to add further comments.[2] The oilmen clearly felt frustrated by the forced-choice questions of the survey, and were concerned that their views were being distorted. For example, when asked whether they agreed with the statement "without sweeping changes in our economic system, little progress can be made in the solution of social problems", many oilmen would agree with the statement, but not in the way that the (presumably liberal) phraser of the question meant. Oilmen feel that there should be sweeping changes made to create a more *laisser-faire* system, not the more socialistic system that they assumed the statement implied. Similarly, in the question on political affiliation, some respondents pointed out that, although they supported the Progressive Conservative party, they did so merely because they considered it to be the least of three evils. From their perspective, Pierre Trudeau was only slightly less socialistic than David Lewis, and Peter Lougheed was not far behind! As one respondent wrote: "I am violently anti-socialism and, therefore, very anti-Trudeau, but not necessarily Conservative."

Strong emotions often lead to irrational opinions. The following statement from a questionnaire is worth recording, not because it is typical of oilmen's views, but because it does represent the kind of feeling that swept their occupational community in 1974.

> I am violently opposed to the ruthless and vicious confiscatory tax policies of the federal government—both against the resource industries and against the middle-income group. The present iniquitous system would be unbelievable in a so-called democracy—if it didn't already exist! It is not tax reform but a dictatorial effort to complete social reform—inept and malicious. What happened to the "work ethic", to pulling your own weight, to expecting fair recompense for training, effort, and initiative? No one minds helping out the unfortunate, the mentally retarded, the physically disabled—but I, for one, object strongly to being taxed to support the lazy or drug-sotted culture so dear to the hearts of Ottawa officialdom.

Other comments showed a more genuine attempt to come to grips with and understand the governments' new involvement and control, but reflected the same bemused bewilderment at what was happening and the same conviction that all was changing for the worse.

> After thirty-five years in the oil business in which I felt I played a part in greatly improving the Canadian standard of living by helping to find energy to supply our own needs and to export and thus help our balance of payments, I find myself becoming more and more pessimistic and disheartened by the present actions of provincial and federal politicians who are treating the oil industry and its employees as if they were a dangerous disease that has to be "stamped out" at all costs.

An American who had lived in Calgary for twenty-three years, had a Canadian wife, and had previously decided to stay but was now about to leave added a typewritten statement to his questionnaire in which he documented the series of moves by provincial and federal governments which he felt proved their immorality (breaking contracts) and commitment to state enterprise (Lougheed's purchase of Pacific Western Airlines). He concluded:

> In short, the credibility of both levels of government is gone as far as I am concerned. It is impossible to make plans for even the near future, say thirty days. Economic projections are useless in trying to evaluate a project because the ground rules are never allowed any semblance of constancy. A politician goes to bed with a headache and the next day all the rules change. A very poor business climate to operate in—reminds one of the "banana republics".

These unsolicited comments reveal the depth of the emotional reaction stirred up within the Calgary oil community in 1973 and 1974, as federal and provincial governments and the informed public attempted to adapt to a radically changed world-energy situation initiated by the members of the Organization of Petroleum Exporting Countries. Part of this attempt to adapt took the form of an attack upon the hitherto undisturbed Canadian oil industry. But before describing and assessing this "crisis" in more detail, we need to understand the oilman's world-view more systematically.

THE MYTH OF FREE ENTERPRISE

I have called the free-enterprise world-view a myth because it distorts reality as much as it represents it. We have seen, for example, that oil prices have never been set by the "free market", and that majors and small oil companies are not fairly competitive with one another. I will add some sympathetic comments about the world-view later, but will first describe it as an ideal type. Collectively, what do oilmen view as being the ideal working economic system and society?

Individualism

Although they hold the idle rich in some disdain (but not as much disdain as the idle poor), oilmen ignore or play down the way in which the institution of private property structures opportunities unequally for Canadians. They believe that, regardless of one's background and beginnings, a man's eventual position in society depends upon his ability, ambition, and willingness to work hard. Within the business world, those that succeed deserve to be wealthy. In the oil industry itself this is reflected in the spirit of competition which dictates that the loser must recognize the legitimacy of the winner; and within the major companies in the notion of legitimate oligarchy, where rumblings of discontent are dismissed as "sour grapes".

Risk-Taking and the Notion of Fair Returns

Oilmen view their industry as being like most capitalist enterprises, with one important exception: the risks are greater. This is part of their faith, rather than a proven fact, but it is empirically grounded for them by the evidence that many small companies continually go out of business, and most wildcat wells drilled fail to strike oil. Those that become rich deserve their good fortune as a reward for taking risks. Just as senior executives deserve large incomes as a fair return for their special entrepreneurial and managerial skills, so those that put up the capital deserve a large return for having taken a gamble. Oilmen choose to ignore the underlying reasons why some individuals have large sums of capital to risk, the way in which lenient tax laws minimize the actual risk involved, and the fact that most investment is done by large corporations that minimize their over-all risks by spreading their drilling eggs among many exploration baskets.

The notion of fair returns helps explain Canadian oilmen's attitudes towards foreign investment. On the one hand, they consider themselves to be good Canadians, and would ideally like to see a greater proportion of their industry owned by Canadians. On the other hand, they attribute the successful growth of the Canadian oil industry largely to foreign, mainly American, investment; and consistently argue that the foreign investors deserve a fair return on their investment. Furthermore, they deplore the reluctance of Canadian capitalists to invest in their industry, attributing it partly to eastern-Canadian prejudice and partly to a federal tax regime that has not permitted individual Canadian investors the same tax advantages as their American counterparts.

Competition, Profits, and Efficiency

The central tenet of the oilmen's faith is expressed simply in the words of one survey respondent as follows: "I strongly believe that the free-enterprise, profit-motivated industries provide the most efficient production of goods and services." There is, for the oilmen, a straightforward and direct cause-and-effect relationship between competition and efficiency. The spirit of competition, and the constraints upon behaviour induced by the imperative to make profits, force oil companies, large and small, to be efficient. The relationship between competition and efficiency (oilmen believe), particularly the role of profits, is misunderstood by critics, governments, and the general public. While it may be true that some people, including foreigners, are unduly enriched by oil companies' profits, this should *not* be viewed as a serious flaw requiring the destruction of the system, but rather as a minor inconvenience that should be ignored for all the benefits that the profit-oriented system entails. Profits, as the major source of accumulated capital, fuel the industry's rapid growth, its high level of job creation, and its ability to provide the good life to western Canadians. Furthermore, and this is even more important and more overlooked by the critics, the desire for profits provides the initiative and the discipline that make the competitive, capitalist oil industry efficient. State-run enterprise lacks that initiative and discipline, and is therefore inefficient. If the Canadian oil industry were nationalized tomorrow, there would be a small saving of the outflow of dividends to foreign capital; but that saving would be miniscule compared to the in creased expenses incurred in setting up a centralized, monstrously bureaucratized, state-run enterprise that could finance its inefficiencies from the public purse; and the costs of energy production and distribution in Canada would increase immeasurably. That is the oilman's faith and the central cause of his concern about the future of his industry.

The Role of Government

Oilmen believe in *laisser faire*, not in the strict sense, but in the sense that governments should not themselves become involved in running industrial enterprises. They do, however, have three important roles: to regulate, to facilitate, and to provide incentives to private enterprise. The regulatory role is exemplified by the Alberta Energy Resources Conservation Board, which oilmen assess very highly. (See Table 2:1, p. 29.) Through its regulations, the Board has enforced a rational program of exploration and production of Alberta's oil and gas resources over the years, and is currently improving its regulations and controls for protecting the natural environment from petroleum-related pollution. Oilmen grumble about some of these regulations and the paperwork they entail, but on the whole, they view their relationship with the AERCB (which entails the government agency's providing over-all regulation but leaving the running of the industry's operations to the oilmen) as the ideal partnership between government and industry.

As facilitator, the government's role is to create those conditions which make profitable enterprise possible should "natural" market conditions preclude this. This, of course, is contradictory to the professed belief in the sovereignty of the market, but oilmen are quick to ignore that belief when it is profitable to do so. The best example of this facilitating role in Canada was the federal government's creation of the Ottawa Valley line in 1961, which opened up Ontario markets to western-Canadian crude oil when it could not otherwise have competed with cheaper foreign crude, and thereby enabled the rapid growth of the Canadian petroleum industry in the 1960s and early 1970s.

Finally, as providers of incentives, the role of governments is to develop tax laws that encourage exploration and production of indigenous sources of crude oil and natural gas. Rather myopically, oilmen assume that the rapid development of such resources is automatically in the national interest. Not only, they argue, does it provide for energy needs in the domestic economy, but the exports that such development makes possible contribute to a healthy balance of payments. Conservation is not a problem because, in the short term, the revenue from exports can finance further exploration and, in the long term, new forms of energy will be found to replace petroleum.[3] Canadian oilmen criticize the federal government, particularly, for failing to match the American government's liberal taxation laws, and claim that the proportion of Canadian ownership in our petroleum industry would be higher had the government followed their advice.[4]

Bureaucracy, Welfarism, and the Decline of the Work Ethic

Complementing their view of a well-functioning economic system and society, oilmen have a counter-view that expresses their fear and concern about the imminent decline of the Canadian economy, society, and moral order. This view is not simply a negative utopia, but expresses what they feel is already happening to their cherished way of life. The adjective they use most often to refer to this decline is "socialistic", although they show little knowledge of the historical roots or philosophical principles of socialist theory. To them, socialism means three things: a growing state bureaucracy and increasing government involvement in industry, the emergence of the welfare state with its big-brother-like cuddling of the individual from cradle to grave, and the decline of the work ethic and its related values.

These concerns bring us full circle, because statism and welfarism conflict most directly, in the oilmen's view, with individualism. Oilmen believe that most people who fail to "make it" in Canadian society do so because of some character weakness or moral flaw—they are too lazy, too stupid, too drunk, or too drugged to do an honest day's work. Furthermore, they have been trained to blame "the system" for their personal problems, and have been encouraged in this by federal and provincial governments that support them with unemployment benefits, welfare payments, free training programs, etc.

Such people should be distinguished from a smaller group of the genuinely poor, those whose poverty is the result of honest misfortune. The "ideal poor", in this sense, are defenseless widows and innocent children. The oilmen's views here are Victorian. The genuine poor deserve our charity which should be administered through voluntary, usually church-related, associations. The able-bodied poor do not deserve the welfare that is administered to them by secular government institutions. The oilmen's view is Victorian as well, I think, in its remoteness from, and hence harshness towards, the realities of structurally induced poverty within contemporary capitalist societies.

DEVIANT VIEWS

In the above section, I have constructed an "ideal type" of the oilmen's world view. Although this fairly represents the views of the majority, there are some oilmen who disagree with their fellows. Some are critical of the large companies with their foreign domination, and complain that upward mobility is restricted for Canadians because most top management positions are held by Americans. Many Canadian oilmen are concerned about foreign ownership. Although most of these accept it as unfortunate but inevitable, a few feel that positive measures should be adopted to improve the situation, although few oilmen would go so far as the following speaker:

> Foreign control of our nation's economy and undue foreign influence on our media, educational institutions, culture, etc., is my prevailing concern. To regain control of Canada's petroleum industry, I fear I have little faith in Canadian corporations and feel that we can only achieve Canadianization by government intervention.
>
> Though my relationship with my company is more than satisfactory and my job, in the short term, is rewarding, the ambivalence of working for an American-owned and controlled company is distressing. Though I am sure that my company considers itself a good corporate citizen, their view of what is good for Canada differs so markedly from mine that I can no longer identify with their goals, and job satisfaction suffers accordingly.

The existence of such minority views is an important reminder that the ideal/typical world-view constructed above is *not* mechanically determined by the oilmen's place in the economic structure. Oilmen are thinking beings who, in their careers, share similar experiences and a similar perspective upon their larger society. They construct their interpretations of reality accordingly, sharing points of view with one another and adopting those ideas from textbooks, popular literature, periodicals, and newspapers that seem to accord with their experience. Their interpretations of experience and their values were challenged, they believed, in the early 1970s. A consideration of their crisis will round out our attempt to grasp the nature of the oilmen's existential reality.

COMMUNITY IN CRISIS

In the fall and winter of 1973, a series of events occurred which drastically altered the political economy of international oil—the so-called "oil crisis". These events reverberated throughout Canada in 1974 and 1975 as the federal and provincial governments scrambled and fought to adjust to the new conditions in ways that best served their own perceived interests. Canada became a microcosm of the international oil struggle, with producing regions asserting a newly found bargaining power against consuming regions, and a bewildered oil industry caught between competing governments and facing an angry, ill-informed, and distrustful public. In the next chapter, I will offer some interpretations of the impact of the crisis at both the international and the national levels. Our present concern is to describe its effects upon the Calgary oil community. In the short term, they suffered an economic setback in which their material interests were directly undermined. More profoundly, they suffered a crisis of community identity in which they genuinely felt, rightly or wrongly (probably the latter), that their cherished way of life was in jeopardy.

First, a chronicle of events.[5] Although the groundwork for change had been laid earlier, the first shock to the major oil companies and Western consuming nations came in September 1973 when Libya nationalized 51 per cent of the interests of its Exxon subsidiary and seven other foreign oil companies. Then the changing economic order became confused with politics when an Arab-Israeli war began on October 6. On October 16, the Arab producers raised the posted price of crude oil from $3.011 to $5.119 per barrel; and this was followed by an agreement to cut exports to countries friendly to Israel and put an embargo on oil exports to the United States and the Netherlands. Although the cuts and embargoes were short-lived, the free-market price of oil shot up dramatically, and this encouraged the OPEC countries to raise the posted price of crude to $11.651 effective January 1, 1974.

Canadian governments had always been so generous and lenient to the oil companies that the national oil policy was dubbed by one critic in 1961 as the "multinational oil policy" (Debanné, 1978: 44). Decisions about pricing and supply had been left to the oil companies, although changing world-market conditions, which gave greater bargaining power to the old producing areas, were beginning to be met by a gradual movement towards greater government control by the early 1970s. The OPEC actions forced a much more rapid modification of the old *laisser-faire* policies. Eastern Canada (part of Ontario, Quebec, and the Atlantic provinces) was wholly dependent upon imported crude from the OPEC countries. The dramatic price increase caused a serious imbalance in the price of oil between eastern and western Canada. The western provinces demanded price increases in line with the new world price, while eastern consumers demanded that the federal government provide some protection from the large price increases and the threatened cutbacks in supplies. The federal government had to try to balance these conflicting interests while wanting, at the same time, to fill its own coffers with a share of the new oil revenues.

The main policy changes were as follows.[6] In January of 1973, *before* the OPEC-induced crisis, Alberta announced a new royalty structure raising the average royalty rate from 16 to 22 per cent. It was stated that this regime would last for five years, but in October of 1973, as the international drama was unfolding, it announced that this would be overhauled. Early in 1974, the province raised its royalty rates so that it would collect 65 per cent of the price in excess of $4.41 per barrel. Higher royalty rates were also announced for natural gas. In the meantime, also late in 1973, Saskatchewan announced a royalty surcharge of about 83 per cent on future price increases, meaning that, together with the basic rate of 17 per cent, the province would collect around 100 per cent of any future increases, leaving no extra profit to the companies; and British Columbia established the British Columbia Petroleum Commission which would take over natural-gas marketing from the oil companies and appropriate future increases in natural-gas prices.

Not to be outdone in this scramble for revenues, the federal government announced in May 1974 that it intended to make royalties and taxes to provincial governments non-deductible for income-tax purposes. This was considered a black day in the oil industry and, after a federal election that saw a Liberal victory despite the Progressive Conservatives' sweep of Alberta, the new measure was passed in November 1974. The allowable rate for claiming development expenditures by the industry was also reduced from 100 to 30 per cent.

The members of the Canadian oil industry, living cosily in Calgary with little knowledge of the international politics of oil, were totally unprepared for this series of events. With some justification, they felt themselves to be unfairly caught in the middle of conflict between governments. After a decade of unrestricted expansion, they suddenly lost control over oil pricing, were told to cut back their production for export to the United States, found themselves having to pay vastly increased royalties and taxes, and saw the formation of what they feared more than anything else—state oil companies in Canada. No wonder that many felt that their world was threatened, indeed coming to an end.

> The climate, in British Columbia, for example, is disastrous. You know, . . . I find [this] a very confusing situation; I can't understand what the various levels of government are expecting to do or what benefits they are expecting to derive out of some of these tax situations, which makes it very difficult to develop areas. There is no such thing as a long-term contract with governments; they can change them overnight. They have just knocked everything we have ever done into an economic catastrophe.

In the short run, the oilmen's psychological fears were reinforced by a genuine decline in their revenues, at least in certain areas and for certain companies. This was the case during the period after the federal government began taxing royalties and before the provincial governments had had time to adjust their new royalty schemes to the federal ploy. For a short time, despite the price increase, some companies were receiving less per barrel of oil than they had done previously. In Saskatchewan, they pointed out indignantly, they were actually losing money on each barrel they produced.

The oil companies were surprisingly unsuccessful in their

initial political lobbying, but they did have a trump up their sleeve. In what radical commentators would call a classic strike of investment, they began to cut down their spending on new exploration. For reasons that we have seen (pp. 19-21), these cutbacks severely affected many drilling, service, and consulting companies in Calgary. Exploratory drilling declined markedly and a number of rigs were moved to the United States, where activity was picking up in response to President Nixon's self-sufficiency policies. In the meantime, Canadian governments were becoming more sophisticated and knowledgeable about the country's energy scene and had learned that proven reserves of oil and gas were much less than they had been led to believe by the industry during the 1960s. More exploration, not less, was required, and the oil companies were the only ones equipped to do it, at least in the short term. Royalty and tax rates were adjusted accordingly to ensure the companies a handsome return on their investments.

In December 1974, Alberta reduced the tax burden on the industry to the tune of a projected $2.5 billion over the period 1975–79. Saskatchewan also agreed to rebate a portion of the increased tax liabilities due to the federal government's new non-deductibility of royalties. In June 1975, the federal government introduced a series of modifications to reduce its share of the revenue somewhat; in July, Alberta reduced its effective royalty still further, and Saskatchewan—and later British Columbia—also lowered their royalty rates and introduced programs to raise the companies' returns. Despite differences in political ideology (the NDP were in power in British Columbia and Saskatchewan, the Progressive Conservatives in Alberta, and the Liberals in Ottawa), it is clear that the behaviour and policies of each government were ruled by economic self-interest, as they came into conflict with, and made accommodations to, each other and the oil industry.

As a result of the governments' partial capitulation to the companies, geophysical-exploration and drilling rates increased again (Figure 7:2). Figure 7:2 also shows a dramatic decline in northern exploration, owing partly to the federal government's delay in announcing new policy guidelines for the north, partly to the uncertain future of the industry's proposed northern pipelines, and partly to the disappointing results of recent exploration in the region. Alberta is enjoying a new exploration

FIGURE 7:2   Exploration Activity (Geophysical)

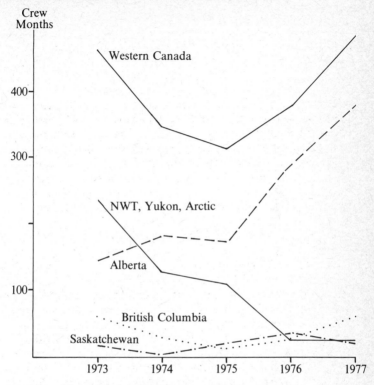

SOURCE: Adapted from *Oilweek*, July 18, 1977, p. 30.

boom as a result both of this decline and of the increased prices for crude oil and natural gas which make formerly marginal fields economically attractive. The continued strength of Alberta throughout the period, and the recent resurgence of British Columbia following the election of a Social Credit government, show how the industry distrusts and punishes provinces that elect NDP governments, despite the evidence cited above which suggests that each government acted pragmatically during the crisis rather than in terms of political ideology. The NDP in Saskatchewan have come to terms with the oil companies. As one senior energy official said to me: "We had to learn that 'profit' is not a dirty word."

The upshot of the new policies was that the crisis passed for the oil community, although their free-enterprise myth has been permanently undermined to some extent. They will probably never again come as close to enjoying *laisser faire* free-enterprise as they did in the fifties and sixties. On the other hand, a new element has been added to their ideology. Large profits are needed, they now maintain, not so much because investors deserve them, but because they are vital to finance the expensive exploration required to ensure the country's future security of petroleum supplies.

CONCLUSION: THE FREE-ENTERPRISE MYTH IN PERSPECTIVE

The oilmen of Calgary believe in the economic system that they refer to as "free enterprise" genuinely and passionately. Yet, any systematic statement of the principles of that system, as conceived by the economists that oilmen rely upon for their ideas, is open to easy rebuttal as a representation about how their economic system really works. Except for a few chaotic years early in the history of the industry, crude-oil prices have never been set by the free play of supply and demand on an open market. They have, rather, been administered prices. Until 1973, they were administered in oligopolistic fashion by the major oil companies. Small producers could not bargain with their buyers over price, they simply accepted what the majors offered. This is not to say, as some critics suggest, that market forces were irrelevant to price. The majors took supply-and-demand considerations into account, but their overriding concern was to set prices at such a level that their profits would provide sufficient capital to finance further expansion and to satisfy their shareholders. As Edith Penrose has pointed out (1968), oilmen's arguments against state companies for risking the public's money are spurious, for it has been the public (as consumers) that has financed industry exploration through paying oligopolistic prices. The recent change to government-administered pricing is not as radical as the oilmen initially feared. Indeed, it has benefited them by ruling out even the possibility of competitive pricing within the industry.

Similarly, free-enterprise ideology about the "correct" relationship between government and private business fails to stand up empirically in the oil business. Since the early Turner Valley days in Alberta, government has been actively involved in the Canadian oil industry—rationalizing its daily operations through the various energy boards, sponsoring the development of both domestic and foreign markets for western-Canadian crude, promoting and subsidizing the construction of continental pipelines, financing research and training, and providing various tax incentives and generous depletion allowances. In addition, governments have had to protect society from the ravages that a truly free-enterprise system would have entailed. This is particularly the case for environmental protection and pollution control. Given the right to pursue their material interests unrestrainedly, the oil companies would have proceeded to destroy the environment. Ecological wisdom is costly, not profitable. Contrary to their own public-relations claims, the oil companies would not have developed their present level of environmental concern without the pressure of governments. Their unanimous support for the Mackenzie Valley pipeline, despite the environmental risks and social costs it would have entailed, has made this single-minded, economic self-interest visible to a public that is becoming better informed and, understandably, increasingly sceptical of the oil companies' motives.

For reasons such as these, the free-enterprise myth is dismissed out-of-hand by many critics of the oil industry and by an increasing proportion of the general public. Despite its contribution to the internal solidarity of the oil community, the myth is detrimental to oilmen's attempts to convey a positive image of themselves and to win sympathy for their concerns from those outside the industry. Because certain aspects of the free-enterprise claims are clearly misleading and contrary to the public interest, people tend to reject them completely. But this entails the danger of throwing out the baby with the bathwater, for it does not follow that, because some of what the oilmen are saying is myopic and narrowly self-interested, *all* of what they are saying must be rejected.

Furthermore, although oilmen believe passionately in the myth of free enterprise, they themselves do not believe in it literally. It is best seen as a symbolic statement expressive of their commitment to their economic system and occupational community. Individually, many oilmen recognize a need for over-all government planning for the future security of energy supplies for the nation, for protecting the environment, and even for ensuring that a fair share of oil profits go to the people of Alberta and the people of Canada. As oilmen point out, they are citizens, too, and share concerns with their fellow citizens as well as their fellow oilmen. This role conflict often induces ambivalent feelings and ideas, as on the issue of foreign ownership. Most Canadian oilmen would like Canadians to be the majority shareholders in the industry. Within the logic of capitalism, however, they cannot see how such a change of ownership could be brought about. Foreign ownership is a cost that they are willing to pay, and is much to be preferred to nationalization by the Canadian state with the attendant centralization, bureaucratization, and inefficiency that they feel would result from it. Nevertheless, they continue to feel uncomfortable about foreign ownership.

The free-enterprise myth, then, is best seen, not as a true picture of the oilmen's economic system or even of what they fundamentally believe, but rather as a general, conceptual framework within which they express their rhetorical allegiance to their community and way of life. This rhetoric is now coming to haunt them, not only because others do not believe it but, more importantly, because it prevents them from communicating the underlying messages they want to convey. Governments were forced to adopt more lenient policies towards the companies in the recent crisis not because they became convinced by what oilmen were telling them, but because they were forced by circumstances (including the investment strike) to recognize their dependency upon the industry. To turn Marx's famous phrase around, the oil companies are the energy arm of the federal and provincial governments. But these may continue to develop their own alternative organizations for energy development, particularly if the oil industry carries on expressing its views in terms of an outmoded free-enterprise rhetoric.

What the oilmen of Calgary are really trying to protect and defend is not some theoretical economist's vision of *laisser faire* free enterprise, but rather the concrete economic system in which they work and the way of life it provides for them. Their concern is with their community and with their identities as members of that community. Most oilmen are salaried workers, not capitalists. They are not concerned about protecting capitalism out of their own propertied self-interest. Nor are they simply duped into a mindless false consciousness by their capitalist bosses and their intellectual ideologues. On the contrary, what they want to protect as good within the system we have described is what it provides for them quite *independently* of private property, profit-making, or even foreign ownership. For them, the system provides comfortable incomes, job security if they do their jobs well, and the luxury of a variety of choices at various stages in their careers—in short, meaningful work and a meaningful life. Perhaps the key term is the old liberal idea of personal freedom, but freedom in a social-structural sense in which the individual can choose his work and career path rather than have it imposed upon him by bureaucratic rigidity. The oilmen also genuinely believe that the system serves not only their own job and career interests, but also their society's interest in having an efficient system for finding, producing, transporting, refining, and delivering petroleum supplies. They insist that competition, the division of labour among majors, small companies, drilling companies, service companies, and consultants, and the adaptability and flexibility that this structure makes possible provide for the country's needs more effectively than could some alternative system.

This is what oilmen believe; and the objections raised by critics of the capitalist Canadian oil industry do not really deal with these issues. They focus upon foreign ownership, profits, and the oligopolistic domination by the majors. All of these are important issues (and are understated by the oilmen), but they do not come to grips at all with the issue of what organizational form the Canadian oil industry should have. Imperial Oil is a very large company, but even so, it produces only about 15 per cent of the country's crude oil; much of the work involved in this production is done by smaller contractees, and the other Canadian producers are all much smaller than Imperial. This organizational format is clearly more decentralized, more flexible, and probably more responsive to local needs than a nationalized industry in which a single, huge, centralized state company would produce 100 per cent of our petroleum. No doubt the latter would also be a less satisfying place in which to work for most of its employees. The critics are right in their criticisms, but have devoted too little attention to alternative organizational forms, and are too simplistic in their proposed solutions.

CHAPTER EIGHT

Conclusion: The Oil Industry and Canadian Society

My aims throughout the body of this work have been to describe and analyse the social organization of the exploration and production phases of the Canadian oil industry and to examine its implications for the careers, levels of job satisfaction, and beliefs of entrepreneurial, managerial, and professional oilmen living in Calgary. This approach, grounded in primary data from interviews, direct observation, and a survey, has entailed the cultivation of a sympathetic account of the industry and its oilmen—towards the functional rather than the dysfunctional aspects of social organization and towards a world-view that reflects the oilmen's experiences and interests.[1] I make no apology for this. The perspective is an important one and deserves our serious attention; particularly as the rhetorical free-enterprise utterances of the CPA, IPAC, and spokesmen for the major oil companies have stood in the way of the industry's receiving enough of this type of analysis and have probably done its image more harm than good.

The social scientist, however, should be more than simply a spokesman for the people he or she investigates. *Verstehen* is not enough. The oilmen's view is clearly one-sided, and cannot be taken as the basis for future policy-making and regulation in the interests of Canadian society as a whole. In this chapter, I will step outside of the oilmen's perspective, contrast it to that of their major critics, present critiques of both views, and attempt to develop a broader, more balanced perspective for understanding the industry and shaping future oil and gas policies in Canada.[2]

THE VIEW OF THE CRITICS

It is useful to start with a view that contrasts sharply with that of oilmen themselves. There exists a long-standing, volumi-

nous, and growing literature criticizing the international petroleum industry from both liberal and radical (Marxist) perspectives. Liberals are concerned mainly with issues of the industry's size, scope, international independence, and the monopoly
power of the major oil companies (Engler, 1961, 1977; Odell,
1970; Hartshorn, 1962). Radicals agree with these points, but
from within a wider theoretical framework in which the oil companies are seen as agents of contemporary capitalist imperial-
ism exploiting Third World countries and appropriating their
economic surplus for the dominant Western powers, particularly the United States (O'Connor, 1955, 1963; Carlo, 1977).
The oil crisis of 1973 – 74 is seen by them as a conspiracy
between the majors and the oil-producing countries to increase
their profits at the expense of Western consumers. The upshot
has been a new integration of the OPEC countries into the
world capitalist system. They are admittedly richer, but at the
cost of having become even more dependent upon the Western
financial and industrial system than they were before (Carlo,
1977).

Canada, in recent years, has seen the growth of a critical
literature that attempts to apply the underdevelopment model
to Canadian society. The country is viewed as an exploited
hinterland of the United States—a source of raw materials for
American industry and a ready market for exports of finished
goods from south of the border. This has entailed a high
degree of direct foreign ownership, a continual drain of economic surplus, the chronic underdevelopment and even decline
of indigenous Canadian industry, the erosion of Canadian entrepreneurship, the Americanization of Canadian culture, and
a serious compromising of political sovereignty (Levitt, 1970;
Government of Canada, 1972). The foreign-owned oil industry
is seen as one of the major culprits in this system, and we now
have a growing radical literature on various aspects of the
industry (Freeman, 1966; Laxer, 1970, 1974; Pratt, 1976; Laxer
and Martin, 1976). The radical movement was formalized in
the establishment of the Public Petroleum Association of Canada (PPAC) in 1975. The Association includes both liberal and
radical critics, although the latter have dominated so far.[3]

For the purposes of this book, I will outline the critics'
position as if it were a single left-wing point of view,[4] but it
should be kept in mind that the PPAC's membership is not

homogeneous and that widely differing political ideologies and
perspectives are represented in it. The radical critics maintain
that the oil industry in Canada suffers from two fundamental
defects that prevent it from serving the public interest: it is
capitalist, and it is foreign-owned. As units within a capitalist
industry, they say, oil companies are privately owned by rich
shareholders intent on becoming richer. The way to become
richer is through the distribution of dividends, a sharing out of
the companies' profits among its shareholders. The companies,
therefore, are profit-oriented. Profits are maximized in three
ways: by keeping costs low, by keeping prices high, and by
expanding the enterprise as a whole.

Each of these profit-making techniques, the critics maintain,
is contrary to the public interest, and they present evidence to
support their contentions. I will outline their main arguments
in each case. Keeping costs low, which was accomplished in
the early years of industrial capitalism by paying very low
wages, is achieved with new, more sophisticated techniques in
contemporary monopoly capitalism. In particular, costs are
"externalized" to the public purse, and this accounts for the
new close relations between corporate enterprise and the state.
The best example of this on the recent Canadian oil scene was
the Syncrude consortium's wresting of financial support and
guarantees from federal and provincial governments before it
would proceed with the construction of a plant for producing
crude oil from the Alberta tar sands near Fort McMurray. The
consortium (originally comprising Imperial Oil, Gulf, Cities
Service, and Atlantic Richfield) gradually inflated its cost estimates for the project from $500 million to close to $2 billion
and, after the withdrawal of Arco whose parent company was
suffering from a capital-shortage problem in the U.S., threatened to abandon the project if its demands were not met.
Premier Lougheed of Alberta was committed to the project as
living proof that his industrialization plan was beginning to
work and as a source of new employment; the federal government had become concerned that Canada's energy reserves (as
estimated mainly by the oil companies) were being depleted;
and the Ontario government shared this concern. The three
governments agreed to provide equity and loan capital to the
project. This was supplemented by generous tax concessions
which meant that, effectively, governments were providing 75
per cent of the capital costs in return for 30 per cent ownership

(Pratt, 1976: 177). In addition, the Alberta government agreed to bear the costs of providing infrastructure for the project, and passed special legislation to allow a no-strike, no-lockout agreement at the site; and the federal government agreed, first, that the oil produced could be sold at the world price for petroleum rather than the lower domestic price, and second, that production would be exempt from any future prorationing. In short, the governments assumed most of the risk and most of the financing, and ensured the future profitability of the project to the consortium; and their 30 per cent participation guarantees that they will be sympathetic to any future demands by the member oil companies. So much for free enterprise!

The second technique for maintaining high profit rates is to charge high prices for one's products. The critics point out that the price of Canadian crude oil has always been higher than either production costs or free-market pressures of supply and demand would require. Before 1973, the price of western-Canadian crude was set on a formula basis to compete with the price of foreign oil landed in the United States at the Gulf of Mexico and shipped to Chicago. But that price itself was inflated to permit higher-cost domestic oil in the U.S. to compete with foreign oil; and it meant that Canadian oil, cheaper to produce than American oil, was overpriced accordingly. Furthermore, the industry lobbied successfully against extending a Canadian pipeline to eastern Canada so that it could continue to supply its eastern refineries with low-cost oil imported into Montreal and to sell the refined products at the inflated North American prices. With the dramatic increase in world prices in 1973, and the governments' taking over of crude-oil pricing, the industry immediately began to lobby the governments of the producing provinces for higher domestic prices. To support their case, industry sources began to alter radically their estimates of remaining petroleum reserves. Reserves were estimated to be abundant during the 1960s, thereby supporting the industry's drive for unlimited exports; but the new estimates told of an impending crisis as Canada ran out of conventional supplies of crude oil and natural gas. The only solution was to increase exploration and development of the expensive sources of petroleum in the tar sands, in the northern frontiers, and in the east-coast offshore areas of Canada. Higher prices were the incentive that would make this possible. The federal government has apparently been convinced by this argument (and has probably also been influenced by its own increased earnings from its share of the higher revenues from crude oil sales), and has accepted in principle the move towards the world price for domestic crude. The critics point out that this price bears no connection at all to the cost of producing western-Canadian crude, that it imposes tremendous hardships upon Canadian consumers, impairs Canada's competitive position in manufacturing, and results in inflationary pressures that imperil the government's own anti-inflation measures. Furthermore, there is no guarantee that the oil companies will use their increased revenues for further Canadian exploration. They could equally well be used for distributing large dividends to shareholders, for furthering exploration in other countries, or for diversifying into other energy (or non-energy) sectors.

The third way to increase profits is through the absolute expansion of the capitalist enterprise; and, as I have argued in Chapter Four, the oil companies are constrained by competition continually to strive for growth. To grow, they must find new markets for their products as supplies increase. During the 1960s, as available Canadian markets became saturated, expansion turned to the huge American market, and the inflated reserves estimates were used to ensure government support for increased exports. There is some confusion in the critics' position about whether exports were simply a natural corollary of capitalist expansion, or whether they were tied into a more explicit continental energy policy involving the complicity of the American-owned oil companies, the U.S. government, and the Canadian government. James Laxer argues the latter case, and points out that such a strategy would be favourable to the United States, which is becoming energy poor, and detrimental to Canada which is energy rich as long as it does not squander its resources through such a continental strategy (Laxer, 1970, 1974). It is not necessary, however, to assume such a conscious policy to explain the high petroleum exports of the sixties and early seventies. They were a natural extension of the capitalist expansion of the Canadian oil industry, and Canadian companies favoured exports as fervently as American companies did. Whatever the cause, there is no doubt that exports grew dramatically to a peak of 1,134,800 barrels daily in 1973, well over half of all Canadian production in that year (*Oilweek*, July 18, 1977: 13). It was only after estimates of petroleum reserves had

been vastly reduced (the government was confidently predict-
ing a 390-year supply of oil in 1971, but only nine years of
proven conventional reserves by 1976) that the federal government intervened to reduce exports. There is little doubt that
Canada's short-term energy supply situation would be much
more favourable today had not so much oil and natural gas
been exported during the past fifteen years.[5]

The critics view the oil industry's advocacy of the Mackenzie
Valley pipeline to carry American gas from Prudhoe Bay in
Alaska and Canadian gas from the Beaufort Sea and the
Mackenzie Delta to southern markets as a further extension of
the continentalist strategy. They point out that proven Delta
reserves are small, and that the foreign-owned companies that
would produce the gas (Imperial, Shell, and Gulf) have already
entered into contracts for *exporting* most of those reserves
(Willson, 1977: 5 – 8). Even a conventional economist, in a
straight cost-benefit analysis, has suggested that 80 per cent of
the benefits of such a pipeline would go to the Americans
(Helliwell, 1977: 1 – 4).

For the critics, foreign ownership and control greatly com-
pound the problems associated with the capitalist nature of the
Canadian oil and gas industry. Foreign ownership—as a mechanism for appropriating Canadian economic surplus in the
form of dividends, management fees, technology and research
levies upon Canadian subsidiaries, imposed costs of imports
from the parent corporations, and accounting practices which
may understate profits in the subsidiaries in favour of the
parent companies—is directly detrimental to the Canadian
economy (Levitt, 1970; House, 1977a). In addition, foreign
ownership imperils the economic and political autonomy of the
Canadian industry. A recent judicial inquiry in Nova Scotia,
for example, uncovered the fact that Imperial's pricing and
crude-oil-supply policies were set by Exxon, and the company
has since admitted that it cannot make expenditures of $50
million or more without parental approval. The critics also
suggest that foreign ownership has developed an unhealthy
dependency upon foreign sources of technology and research
and development. Although I agree that research is underdeveloped in Canada, I have argued above that access to the
majors' transnational technological expertise is a major benefit
of the multinational affiliation (see pp. 56-57). There is as well,

I think, a deeper emotional objection to foreign ownership, a nationalist sentiment that a vigorous, independent country *should* own and control its own vital industries. As I have suggested, this view is shared by many oilmen.

Finally, the critics' objections to the current organization of the Canadian oil industry derive from a wider view of economic, ecological, and social concerns than that taken by most oilmen. This difference can best be illustrated by the recent Mackenzie Valley pipeline dispute. For the oil companies, the situation was straightforward. They needed new sources of supply to satisfy their goals of increased profits and growth; the United States needed gas from Prudhoe Bay; Canada needed both the gas from the Mackenzie Delta—for consumption and for foreign exchange through exports—and the jobs that the huge industrial project would create. The most economical way to meet these various needs was to build the Mackenzie Valley pipeline. *Ergo*, the pipeline should be built, everyone would benefit, and all would be for the best in the best of all possible economic systems. But the situation, as the critics pointed out, was far from that simple. With their unbounded enthusiasm for the project and their belief that capital and technology could conquer all problems, the oil companies glossed over too many difficulties. We have already seen that the project was dubious economically. It was even more dubious ecologically and socially. Justice Thomas Berger's sensitive report makes it clear that the Arctic Gas consortium was prepared to proceed with the project without a proper understanding of the ecological problems it would certainly create, without having solved major technological problems (particularly the danger that frost heave could cause buckling and rupturing of the pipeline), and with little appreciation of the effects of rapid industrialization upon native land claims and the native way of life in the area. In taking these larger considerations into account, Berger recommended that no pipeline should be built from Prudhoe Bay across the northern Yukon, and that there should be a ten-year moratorium before a pipeline could be built along the Mackenzie Valley. Berger was not opposed to oil and gas development as such, but rather to the market mentality which pursued economic progress for its own sake, assuming that the natural environment and society itself would adjust as best they could to this progress. On the contrary, he implied, oil and gas development must be constrained and controlled in terms of these wider concerns, and in terms of the potential of the indigenous economy of the north.

> An economy based on modernization of hunting, fishing, and trapping, on efficient game and fisheries management, on small-scale enterprise, and on the orderly development of gas and oil resources over a period of years—this is no retreat from the past, rather, it is a rational program for northern development based on the ideals and aspirations of northern native peoples. (Berger, 1977: XXVI)

Such a conclusion could never come from the oilmen; as the critics rightly point out, the current social organization and policies of the oil industry take no thought for the relationship between energy policy and wider social concerns. Unfortunately, however, the critics are not very clear about how the system should be changed. They argue for a conversion to some form of public ownership and state control—through a buy-back program, participation arrangements, outright nationalization, or the conversion of the oil companies to public utilities. But neither the mechanism for doing this nor the way the industry would be organized after it was done are clearly spelled out. While recognizing their valuable contributions to the current energy debate, I think it is necessary to subject the critics' position itself to critical scrutiny.

CRITIQUE OF THE CRITICS: DO WE REALLY WANT A STATE-RUN PETROLEUM INDUSTRY IN CANADA?

Although I am sympathetic to the critics' position, I believe that it is both unduly one-sided and logically and empirically flawed in many of its details. In criticizing their arguments, I will raise a number of issues that I think are important for a more rounded view.

The Monolithic View of the Majors

Critics of both the international and Canadian oil industries tend to see the major oil companies as a unity, conspiring together to control both the world oil market and the governments and people of the countries in which they operate. But a careful reading of oil-industry history contradicts this view. Despite the infamous attempt at Achnacarry in 1928, the majors never succeeded in establishing a tight collusive cartel for controlling crude-oil supply and pricing (although, for a long period, they did manage to establish oligopolistic control).[6] The interests of the various majors were simply too divergent. Not only were they in competition with one another and with outsiders for scarce markets and reserves, but differences among companies, some of which had crude-oil surpluses and some of which had deficits, created conflicting policies and behaviour. Nor have the majors been able to keep competitors out. Competition from Russian oil, the rise of European state companies, and the international expansion of many American independents led to a gradual decline in the majors' share of crude-oil production from 90 to 75 per cent outside North America and the communist countries between 1952 and 1968 (Wilkins, 1975: 162). When a few American independents discovered large reserves of crude oil in Libya in the 1960s, they were forced to sell them at reduced prices to western-European countries, as they had been shut out of their home market by an American policy designed to protect local producers. To protect their market share, the majors were forced to cut prices as well, and the real cost of oil declined throughout the decade, despite the majors' efforts to control it. The presence of the independents also improved the bargaining power of the OPEC producers, as did both the growing dependence of western Europe upon imported crude and the new need for imports in the United States. The majors were not able to control these developments. Although they are powerful, they are not as all-powerful—and certainly not as united—as the critics suggest.

In Canada, critical attention has also been focused upon the majors, and particularly on Imperial Oil Limited. But, as the analysis in chapters Two and Three above clearly shows, such a focus badly distorts the organization and dynamics of the Canadian petroleum industry. The majors are big, but hundreds of other companies are integrally involved in the process of finding and producing oil and gas in this country and of making the system work flexibly and efficiently. Their role should not be simply ignored as irrelevant.

The Evils of Economic Self-interest and Profits

Just as the oilmen's market mentality leads them to assume that pursuing their own best interests will inevitably contribute to the public good, so the critics' collectivist mentality leads them to the equally facile conclusion that behaviour guided by material self-interest can only lead to public harm. The examples of Syncrude, exaggerating reserves to promote exports, and the Mackenzie Valley pipeline lend credibility to this view. These examples, however, have been chosen selectively by the critics. In many other ways, the capitalist oil industry has contributed positively to Canadian society. As consumers, most of us enjoy a reliable source of high-grade heating fuel for our homes and of high-grade gasoline and lubricating oil for our cars. Our industries and public buildings are equally well-served. These facts are so obvious that to mention them seems trite, but they should not be taken for granted. In addition, Alberta and, to a lesser extent, Saskatchewan and British Columbia have grown to prosperity on the coat-tails of the foreign-owned oil industry. It is difficult to envisage how such growth could have been accomplished without the input of foreign capital, expertise, and technology, particularly in the early years. And, as the study reported here clearly shows, the people working in the industry now are mainly Canadians who enjoy fulfilling careers and high levels of job satisfaction. There is no simple formula for equating economic self-interest with either public good or public evil, and perhaps we would now do better to try to devise controls that maximize the former and minimize the latter.

The oilmen's and the critics' views show the same kind of one-sided opposition on the important issue of profits. The critics focus mainly upon the income-distribution function of profits within contemporary corporate capitalism. Through mobilizing raw materials, capital, and labour, the corporation creates profits, a large proportion of which are distributed to shareholders in the form of dividends. Since most shares are held by a small minority of wealthy citizens, the distribution of profits is the major vehicle by which income is expropriated from the non-propertied working class by the propertied class in capitalist societies. Foreign-owned subsidiaries, such as the Canadian majors, pay most of their dividends to their American and European parent corporations, which use these dividends for capitalist expansion in other countries and to further enrich the propertied classes in their own countries. Thus, Canadian enterprise serves to consolidate the wealth and power of the foreign propertied classes in the major metropolitan centres of the world capitalist system. Furthermore, as the critics rightly show, the profit levels of the major oil companies have risen astronomically since the energy crisis, both internationally and within Canada. The rapid price rises in recent years have meant that gross income for western Canada's petroleum industry has risen from $2,189,604,000 in 1972 to an estimated $8,257,000,000 in 1977. With estimated expenditures in 1977 of $7 billion (including $3,020,000,000 in royalties), the industry will enjoy profits of well over $1 billion (*Oilweek*, July 18, 1977, p. 32).

This exploitative function of profits is conveniently ignored by Calgary oilmen, but its other function, upon which they focus, is equally ignored by the critics. Profits are the main source of capital for the majors, and their successful mobilization of capital through large profits has been a predominant reason for their being able to tackle such massive projects as the exploration and development of the North Sea (and, through such projects, to contribute so significantly to industrial growth). Furthermore, if the argument of the oilmen outlined above has any validity (pp. 113-118), profit-making is an important disciplinary force which makes the capitalist system efficient and technologically progressive, thereby contributing to a high material standard of living.[7] This aspect of profit-making is ignored by the critics, but it seems clear to me that profits serve both an exploitative *and* a progressive function within contemporary corporate capitalism. If profits are to be abolished, some alternative mechanisms of capital accumulation and of ensuring organizational efficiency and technological progressiveness must be instituted.[8] The critics pay scant attention to this, thereby falling into a misleading zero-sum-game view of national wealth. It is conceivable that we in Canada could cut off the flow of dividends to foreign oil corporations to the *detriment* of our national wealth, if the alternative form of organizing the industry proved inefficient and technologically backward. This is what the oilmen fear would happen. They may be wrong, but the critics have not proven them wrong. This brings us squarely to the question of alternative forms of economic organization.

THE ALTERNATIVE: A STATE-RUN PETROLEUM INDUSTRY?

To date, the critics of the foreign-owned, capitalist oil industry in Canada have said little about the kind of economic organization that should replace it. The danger in this is that we could find ourselves, by default, drifting towards a centralized, state-run industry that neither meets the requirements of socialist principles nor serves the people of Canada better than the present system. This problem of finding a better alternative has plagued critics of capitalism since Marx himself, and the experiences of eastern Europe, the Soviet Union, and even of Great Britain should warn us that nationalization can create as many problems as it solves.

Although the following discussion is far from conclusive, it is worth considering for a moment the one comparative case that we do have—that of the Soviet Union. Like the foreign-owned, private petroleum industry in Canada, the domestically owned, public industry in the U.S.S.R. has grown rapidly since World War Two, although the Russians are fortunate in having much greater proven petroleum reserves than we do. On the one hand, the successful growth of the oil and gas industries in the Soviet Union is a convincing contradiction of the oilmen's claim that foreign capitalist development is essential in Canada. Nationalization and state-run enterprise is, clearly, a viable option. On the other hand, despite their having been involved in the petroleum industry for a long time, the Soviets have apparently been unable to develop their organizational and technological effectiveness to western levels. Although the evidence is difficult to come by, one analyst has managed to assemble enough data to present a fairly clear picture (Campbell, 1968, 1976). His analysis does suffer, in my opinion, from an ethnocentric bias in comparing the Soviet industry to an idealized market system,[9] but his data on organizational efficiency and technological progress seem free from ideological bias. In assessing the history of Soviet energy policy in general, Campbell is struck by its tardiness in developing petroleum resources and its waste of large amounts of scarce capital in attempting to develop inefficient and esoteric sources of energy.

One might expect that a planned economy would have the advantage of allowing the energy picture to be regarded as a whole and assigning to each energy source and utilization technology its appropriate role. However, the Russians seem to have made serious mistakes in fuel policy. They were slow to grasp the opportunity offered by oil and gas, and they have wasted large amounts of resources on the development of uneconomic energy sources. Their infatuation with the underground gasification of coal and with synthetic liquid fuel are examples. Also, they have themselves now decided that too much attention was paid in the past to the development of hydroelectric energy resources, since cheaper alternatives were available to them. (Campbell, 1968: 15 – 16)

Compared to North America, the oil and gas industry of the Soviet Union has some advantages. Exploration is more rational, with less duplication of geological and seismic mapping, and less hoarding of valuable drilling information.[10] Well-spacing programs have also been more rational, particularly as compared to the United States, where the "law of capture" has meant that wells were placed close together in the attempt to drain oil from reservoirs beneath other private owners' property. This caused an overcommitment of scarce capital and labour to drilling wells, and led to rapid well depletion which reduced ultimate recoverability in some areas. The problem has been largely solved in Canada through unitization schemes imposed by the energy boards. Finally, with respect to advantages, the Soviets have perhaps been more easily able to organize massive capital projects, such as the building of large pipelines from western Siberia to the European U.S.S.R.

Other comparisons, however, favour the West. The Russians progressed rapidly in proving new reserves in the 1960s through developing their own drilling technology, the turbodrill. But new reserves require deeper drilling, and the turbodrill is much less efficient at greater depths than the Western rotary drill. The Russians are also behind in the development of sophisticated compressor systems for their pipelines; and their refinery technology is backward by Western standards. For example, they have only been able to produce 77-octane gasoline compared to 90 for regular gas in the United States. And their gasoline is less volatile or "heavier" which " . . . means difficulty in starting engines, longer periods for warm-up, and greater wear" (Campbell, 1968: 170). Concerned about this technological lag, the Soviets have recently begun negotiating with the Americans to provide natural gas in return for expertise and technology.

The Soviet petroleum industry, as compared to the North American industry, also suffers from organizational inefficiencies. I suggested earlier that the division of labour among operating companies, drilling companies, and service companies, with competition at each level, contributes to the flexibility and efficiency of the industry in Alberta. The centralized, hierarchical Soviet system lacks this flexibility and attendant efficiency. Campbell's data and comments on this deserve serious consideration by advocates of nationalization.

> The low productivity of Soviet drilling rigs and crews is shown by a comparison of *commercial speed* with an approximation of the same concept for the United States. The Russians attained their highest average commercial speed for all drilling in 1958—609 meters per rig per month. In that year the United States average was a little over 1,200 meters per rig per month, and by 1963 it had risen to about 1,600 meters per rig per month. The explanation for low productivity in the U.S.S.R. is the high percentage of unproductive time.... In 1960 only 64 per cent of total rig time was spent actually working, only 13 per cent rotating the bit. Over a third of total rig time was lost in stoppages for repair, stuck tools, fishing operations, dealing with circulation problems, waiting for cement, pipe, and so on.... the Americans apparently lose much less time in breakdowns, repairs, and other wasted time. One Russian source says that productive time is 91 per cent of total time in the American time budget and auxiliary work is only 15 per cent of total time.
>
> *Much of the wasted time is caused by poor organization.* In the Soviet economy any activity which depends on the co-operation of auxiliary units or suppliers is likely to be impeded by breakdowns in supply. Soviet rigs spend a large amount of time waiting for cement or casing, bits, turbodrills, and repair parts for rigs that have broken down. (Campbell, 1968: 91 – 92; my italics)

Comparing the Soviet petroleum industry to the North American, the Soviet industry does not measure up in the ways that I suggested earlier contributed to the economic success of the North American industry. The Soviet industry's forced savings, lagging technology, and inflexible organization produce inefficiency compared to the North American industry's internalized capital accumulation, competitive technology, and flexible organization. And, to the extent to which greater efficiency is passed on to consumers (as in high-octane gasoline), the North American system contributes more to society.

Finally, in assessing the two systems, we should ask the further question: what is it like to work and live in each? I have suggested that Canadian oilmen enjoy their work largely for the organizational and career freedom that the system allows. Comparative data is unfortunately not available for the Soviet Union. Campbell contrasts the Soviets' administratively organized economy in which productive processes are co-ordinated almost entirely by superordinate-subordinate hierarchical communication, with the lateral communication that characterizes much of the co-ordination in a market system. This implies that the Soviet petroleum industry may be a less enjoyable system in which to work.

These comparisons, based on a single case, are far from conclusive, and require further comparative analysis of other cases. An initial consideration of the Mexican petroleum industry, for example, which was nationalized in 1938, suggests that the Soviet experience is not unique. One journalist's impression was reported as follows:

> Pemex (the state petroleum company) . . . is arguably the most corrupt, least efficient organization in Mexico. Jobs in the department have long been considered sinecures. Executive positions are openly sold to incompetents if the bribe money is sufficient. Politicians' wives are routinely "given" one or two Pemex gas stations as gifts, the profits going into private pockets rather than government coffers. Other Mexican government bureaus routinely dump their least effective executives into Pemex positions, where traditionally they have never been heard of, or seen, again. When Mexicans nationalized their oilfields in 1938, they did so under the cry: "The Oil is Ours". The local wisecrack now is that Pemex's employees have adopted the slogan as their very own. (Gonzalez, 1978:25-26)

A nationalized Canadian oil industry may not encounter the same difficulties as the Russian and Mexican. The point is, however, that the likely problems have been all but ignored by the critics. They at least deserve serious consideration, and perhaps we should be thinking about other possible approaches.

Minor Difficulties

Before pursuing the question of possible alternatives to nationalization, there are a few additional problems in the critics' position that should be mentioned. The first has to do with price. It is simplistic to argue that the oil companies are concerned about receiving higher prices. Rather, they are concerned about the share of the price that goes to industry as net income. The prime movers behind the recent price rises were the OPEC countries internationally, and the governments of the western provinces, particularly Alberta, nationally. *Oilweek* estimates that governments will receive over $3 billion in royalties alone in 1977. Governments of oil-producing areas have become major expropriators of economic surplus, and this dominant fact has received too little attention from the critics. It is also striking that, contrary to simple metropolis-hinterland assumptions, the federal government has consistently supported the position of Alberta against Ontario on the issue of price. That apparent contradiction needs more thorough investigation and explanation.

A related weakness in the critics' position is its apparent centrist bias. This is no doubt unintended. The PPAC's statement of purpose recommends that new manufacturing "should be centred as far as possible in the regions of Canada that now concentrate on extractive industries alone—the West, northern Ontario and Quebec, and the Atlantic provinces" (Laxer and Martin, 1976: 253). But the Association's recommended policy of tying petroleum prices to the costs of production and exploration, thereby keeping them well below the OPEC "world price", is intended mainly as a spur to *established* Canadian manufacturing, most of which is located in southern Ontario. Whatever the intention, the implication is that the western provinces should relinquish much of their windfall income for the benefit of manufacturing in Ontario, and that the northern territories and the Atlantic provinces should risk a long-term postponement of the exploration and development of their very costly petroleum resources. The critics' case is partly based upon the justifiable claim that the country has no guarantee that the oil companies will in fact spend their new revenues on further exploration in Canada; and they support this by showing that the level of exploration in 1974 did not increase with the dramatic rise in profits in 1973. But, as I have shown, the industry considered itself to be in crisis at that time and responded by a short-term investment strike. As Figure 7:2 (page 123) shows, exploratory activity has increased markedly since then. Although they are blunt instruments and difficult to control, it does seem that price and tax incentives do stimulate further exploration, even though they also provide further cream for the foreign parent companies and their shareholders.

The PPAC position includes a centrist bias in a constitutional sense as well. In effect, it holds that Ottawa should impose lower prices for oil and gas upon Alberta. But natural resources and, presumably, the wealth created by them, belong to the provinces by the terms of the British North America Act. To what extent can the federal government legally and morally infringe upon that right? Concern about this question no doubt explains why some of the other provinces rich in natural resources, particularly Quebec and Newfoundland and Labrador, have agreed to the higher prices despite the burden they impose upon consumers in their provinces. Again, the issues are more complex and multi-stranded than the critics imply.

The same can be said, I think, for the critics' interpretation of the behaviour and policies of governments generally. We have seen that, from the oilmen's perspective, government regulation and involvement in their industry appears to be increasing unchecked. Again, the critics provide a counterview. They dismiss government efforts either as involving too little too late (as in the phasing out of oil exports), or as simply veiled attempts to further benefit the oil companies (as in the financing of Syncrude). But I think the critics may be failing to see the woods for the trees. Although individual instances of government intervention can be explained away, recent actions taken as a whole suggest that there must be something to the oilmen's worries. Within the past decade, the federal and provincial governments have: taken over the pricing of crude oil and natural gas; taken control of oil and gas exports; set up Crown corporations in each of the producing provinces and in the country as a whole; bought a small Canadian major (Petro-Canada's purchase of Atlantic Richfield Canada Limited); set up a consortium of small Canadian companies with federal equity financing (Panarctic); taken complete control of natural-gas purchasing and marketing (in British Columbia); designated a large natural-gas reserve for development by a provincial energy company (the Suffolk field in Alberta); declared an intention to take a 40 per cent equity interest in offshore producing companies (Newfoundland and Labrador); refused permission for the construction of the Mackenzie Valley pipeline despite a heavy industry lobby; and vastly increased their own royalty and tax incomes from petroleum production. I think it is myopic to dismiss all of these developments as simply a concealed continuation of the nation's long-term sell-out to the foreign-owned oil corporations. Something more is happening. To appreciate better what that is, we need first to re-assess the role of the state within contemporary capitalist societies, particularly with regard to recent trends in government-industry relations on the international petroleum scene.

OIL, THE MIDDLE EAST, AND THE CHANGING WORLD ORDER

In his penetrating analysis of political and economic relations in nineteenth-century Europe, Karl Marx argued that the state was "the political arm of the bourgeoisie". In other words, European governments were essentially the representatives of the dominant economic class of society—the merchant, financial, and industrial capitalists who constituted the bourgeoisie. This insight was particularly helpful for explaining the rise to political power of new men and new parties in Great Britain and their introduction of the policies that helped to produce a market society—i.e., the repeal of the corn laws which transformed agriculture and made land into a commodity, and the repeal of the poor laws which created a national labour market (Polanyi, 1957).

Marx's insight remains a key element in critical social thinking to this day. At the same time, however, it leads to some serious distortions and omissions in Marxist analysis. As Polanyi shows, even in nineteenth-century Britain there was a counter-movement to the disruption of social life by the market system, and this counter-movement also found expression through state legislation, which led, eventually, to the present welfare state. The rapid growth of Western states during this century, particularly their development as major economic powers in their own rights, calls for a re-conceptualization of the relationships between capitalist enterprise and the modern state.

Following Weber (1947) and some more recent works by economic anthropologists and sociologists (cf. Sahlins, 1965; Krohn, *et al.*, 1977), I will view the polity as an independent social institution in its own right with its own social function, dynamics, and people whose pursuit is political rather than economic power. It is not simply a superstructure of an "un-

derlying" economic substructure. In analysing the relations between capitalist states and business corporations, we need to
look not simply at how the former serve the interests of the
latter, but rather at the dynamics and bargainings that characterize the exchange relations between states and business enterprises.

The international history of the Western petroleum industry
might be described as follows.[11] The early years were characterized by a strong coincidence of interests between industrial
states and the emerging multinational major oil companies,
particularly between the British government and Shell and BP,
and between the American government and the five American
majors: Exxon, Standard of California, Mobil, Gulf, and Texaco. The third party in international oil politics was the governments of those under-developed Third World countries,
mainly in South America and the Middle East, where major
petroleum reserves happened to be located. Lacking the capital, technology, and expertise to search for oil themselves, and
desperately hopeful that oil could prove the means to wealth
for the ruling class and to economic development for their
societies as a whole, these Third World states were initially in a
weak bargaining position.

The coincidence of interests between the majors and the
Western states is best illustrated by American policy in the
Middle East. Caught in the dilemma of trying to placate Israeli
and domestic Jewish sentiment, while wanting to maintain a
strong presence in the Middle East against Russian encroachment, the U.S. government implicitly deputized the oil companies as its foreign-relations representatives in that area. In return for accepting this responsibility, again implicitly, the oil
companies were rewarded with generous tax concessions and
exemptions from U.S. anti-trust regulations. This implicit policy worked reasonably well during the early growth of the
petroleum industry in the Middle East.

After World War Two, however, a number of trends
emerged which eventually culminated in a fundamental shift in
bargaining power among the major actors on the world petroleum stage. The rapid industrial growth of western Europe and
Japan created a huge market for energy. These countries are
energy poor themselves, particularly in petroleum. At the same
time, the development of massive petroleum reserves in the
Middle East and, to a lesser extent, North Africa, made the

Western countries and the major oil companies themselves increasingly dependent upon the countries that formed OPEC in 1961. The changing situation was compounded by a short-sighted U.S. domestic policy during the sixties. Misled (as in Canada's case) by inflated industry estimates of remaining reserves, and wanting to protect domestic producers from cheap foreign oil, the United States instituted a system of import quotas. This had two important effects. First, it hastened the depletion of domestic oil and gas reserves, so that the U.S. itself is now dependent upon Middle Eastern oil for a large and growing proportion of its energy requirements. Second, by declaring the American market off-limits to outside oil, it forced the international oil companies, particularly the newly established independents, to seek alternative markets. Blessed with huge reserves in Libya, but desperate to maintain their cash flows, the independents (particularly Occidental) began to sell at reduced prices in European markets. The policy of cheap oil was initially supported by the Arab and African producing countries which wanted increased revenues from expanding sales. To maintain their market shares, the international majors were forced against their will to meet the lower prices. Western Europe and Japan gratefully gobbled up the new supplies, and domestic consumption shifted increasingly to petroleum as the major energy source.

The upshot of all these trends was that, by 1970, North America, western Europe, Japan, and the international oil companies, had all become extremely dependent upon the OPEC producers. Two further ingredients were required to precipitate the crisis of 1973: the OPEC countries had to come to perceive their new bargaining strength for what it was, and they had to develop the unity to put their new power into effect. The Arab-Israeli war of the autumn of 1973 provided the emotional impetus for this new realization and unity. The Arabs, followed by the other OPEC members, dared to defy the Western powers and the oil companies. Their success amazed everyone, including themselves.

In retrospect, it is clear that, in spite of making a lot of noise, there was nothing the consuming nations could do but bear the fruits of their own dependency. Military invasion was out of the question. Not only would it have been rampantly imperialistic, but the Arabs had threatened to blow up their oil fields.

The oil companies, however, although hostile to the new OPEC initiatives and powerless to prevent them, were still much better placed to adapt to them and profit by them than the consuming nations were. Unlike the consuming nations, they still had a trump up their sleeve. This trump was their continuing international control over downstream industry activities: transportation, refining, and marketing. The behaviour of the major oil companies during and after the crisis illustrates clearly that relations between governments and business corporations cannot be correctly conceived in terms of the traditional Marxist model, which views the state as acting in terms of the interests of the companies. The American government, for example, failed to heed any of the warning of top oil-industry officials in the days preceding the crisis. It was too compromised by other pressure groups, particularly the pro-Israeli domestic Jewish community. Nor can subsequent events be understood in terms of the more recent model of capitalist underdevelopment, which tends to view multinational corporations as imperialist agents of their own governments, that is, of the governments in which their head offices and major shareholders are located. Again, this should be viewed as a coincidence of interests where it prevails, rather than as any sort of conscious policy for Western hegemony. The behaviour of the oil companies shows how this coincidence of interests can break down and shift as conditions change.

Despite their early attempts to thwart OPEC's designs, and despite their complaints of government interference, nationalization, participation agreements, and the monopoly prices of the new cartel, the major oil companies have been quick to recognize where their new interests lie, and to ally themselves with their new partners, the OPEC producing countries. It was the oil companies that obeyed the decrees of their new partners, and administered the politically induced embargoes in the winter of 1973 (Stobaugh, 1975: 179 – 202). Against the will of their home government, the American majors refused to move Arabian oil to the U.S.; and even BP defied its own major shareholder, the British government, in deference to the producing countries. And it has, no doubt, been through the co-operation of the majors that the OPEC countries have been so successful in making their price increases and production controls stick. The companies, in return, have been rewarded by long-term contracts for crude-oil supply, and by profit and growth levels that exceed their wildest dreams of a few years ago. What matter to the companies that these have been achieved at the expense of the Western consumer, especially as they can argue, with justification, that their only alternative is to see the control of oil slip more and more out of their hands (Blair, 1976). The majors also took advantage of the energy crisis to discipline the independent producers for their price cutting, and to force many independent retailers in the U.S. out of business. For the first time, what they have been attempting to achieve for many years with only limited and sporadic success—that is, true cartel pricing and control of supply—has been made possible through their alliance with OPEC.

Paradoxically, within a wider perspective, the new economics and politics of world oil have meant a greater, not a lesser, integration of the Middle East into the world capitalist system (Carlo, 1977: 5 – 34). This is because the Arabs must be wary of pressing the Western consuming nations too far. A serious depression would not only affect oil revenues, but would also endanger the massive new investments that the Arabs have been making in Western financial markets and industries. In addition, in their drive for rapid industrialization, the Arabs have been turning to Western multinational corporations to provide the materials, technology, and expertise they require and have found that the capitalist nations of the West are much better equipped to do this than the socialist U.S.S.R. and eastern Europe (*Business Week*, 1975). For the time being at least, a new equilibrium seems to have been established, such that the OPEC nations have considerable influence over the course of world events, while the Western consuming nations enjoy, more or less in spite of themselves, renewed access— although not secure access in the old style—to the world's major source of petroleum supplies. The real losers have been the U.S.S.R., which has had its political influence in the Middle East undermined, and, tragically, the Third World countries that lack petroleum supplies of their own and have been forced to pay the steeper prices.[12]

OIL AND THE CHANGING CANADIAN ORDER

Some understanding of international oil politics is necessary to place the Canadian scene in perspective (and also, of course, to provide an interesting comparison). In many ways, developments in Canada during the past six years have been a microcosm of the larger international changes. The western producing provinces are Canada's OPEC countries, and they, like OPEC, have served in the past as a valuable hinterland source of raw materials for the industrial centres of North America. Alberta is Canada's Saudi Arabia, with Premier Lougheed epitomizing what some bitter American senator facetiously labelled "the blue-eyed Arabs of the north". Southern Ontario and Quebec are the metropolitan centres within the Canadian system that depend upon "imports" of crude oil and natural gas from the western provinces and oil from some OPEC countries (mainly Venezuela). These supplies are essential to their industrial well-being and comfortable living standards. The northern territories and the Atlantic provinces are the "Third World" of Canada—passive pawns in the negotiations among the powerful. The parallel between the international and domestic oil scenes breaks down in one important respect—the presence in Canada of a central political authority. The federal government has tried to reconcile the interests of the conflicting parties and, equally importantly, to further its own federalist power throughout the recent oil and energy negotiations. The fourth party on the Canadian scene, of course, is the Canadian majors, subsidiaries of the same multinationals that dominate the international petroleum industry.

With the dramatic increase in the price of oil in the world markets in 1973, the western provinces, led by Alberta, immediately began to agitate for higher prices for western-Canadian crude oil and natural gas. The federal government, politically dependent upon Ontario and Quebec, initially reacted as one would expect in a metropolis-hinterland situation. It took over the pricing of crude oil and natural gas in interprovincial trade and export markets, as was its legal right according to the BNA Act. It then introduced an ingenious short-term scheme designed to keep prices low for the consuming provinces, to keep Alberta "in its place", and to pay for the increased cost of imported oil in Montreal by levying an export tax on Canadian crude shipped to the United States. In the longer term, to protect Canada's security of supply, it initiated plans to extend the interprovincial pipeline to Montreal so that western-Canadian crude could, if necessary, supply the whole of the country.

This protectionist policy for Canadian industry and consumers was bitterly opposed both by the western provinces and by the oil industry. This opposition was buttressed by the new pessimistic estimates for frontier reserves, the new higher estimates of the costs of exploiting northern and offshore reserves and the Alberta tar sands, and the ominous warning that the supply of conventional reserves in the producing provinces had peaked and was beginning an inevitable decline. Whether or not this information was correct, the important point is that the oil industry held the upper hand in negotiations because of its *control* of information. The federal government could not afford to ignore the industry's warnings, and this proved to be the fly in the ointment for its initial protectionist policy.

Worried about the country's long-term supply of oil, and encouraged by the contribution of higher prices to swelling federal coffers, the federal government has reversed its earlier policy position. Its 1976 policy statement aims for "self-reliance" in energy. In the short-term, this means self-reliance in petroleum, which in turn means a massive national commitment to and investment in petroleum exploration and production. The mechanism for inducing this is to be the blunt instrument of higher prices: [13] "moving domestic oil prices towards international levels; and moving domestic prices for natural gas to an appropriate competitive relationship with oil over the next 2 – 4 years" (Energy, Mines and Resources Canada, 1976: 6). Despite the presence of a central-government authority, then, the outcome of Canada's energy crisis has paralleled that of the international crisis. Like western Europe and Japan, Ontario has had to accept the new prices imposed by the producing regions in consort with the oil companies. Many Albertans are revelling in their new-found power. A bumper sticker prevalent in Calgary a few years ago announced: "Let the eastern bastards freeze." One hopes that they did not mean it, but it expresses the kind of euphoria released now that the exploited have become the exploiters. The biggest losers, again, are the forgotten "Third World" regions. Always disadvantaged by excessive energy prices due to transportation costs and monopolistic local marketing practices, the Canadian consumers in the north and the Atlantic provinces (the ones who can least afford it) must now pay vastly increased prices as their share of the tribute to the Arab states and the western producing provinces.

The consequence of these negotiations and policy decisions

is that Canada's energy prospects are now ruled by an informal triumvirate consisting of the oil companies, the producing provinces, and the federal government.[14] Even so, the actual situation tends to be obscured by ideological cant, differences in political affiliation, and minor squabbles about how the oil-revenue pie is to be shared among the three partners. Albertans still like to talk of themselves as "alienated" and exploited by the east. The federal government claims to be concerned with the interests of consumers. And the oil industry likes to depict itself as the innocent victim, caught in the middle of disputes between governments. Both the federal and provincial producer governments *have* taken measures to improve their access to information and their expertise about the petroleum industry through a measure of direct involvement. But this should not be taken as the beginning of an inevitable trend towards nationalization. Rather, all the parties concerned have settled into a new equilibrium in which the oil companies are equal partners. In return for greatly increased profits, they are expected by their governmental partners to get on with the job of developing new petroleum reserves. They are clearly doing that in Alberta.

The oil companies have managed to exploit their new partnership in a way contrary to the federal government's expressed policy. Rather than use their high profits to increase frontier exploration, they have been pouring them instead into the low-priced conventional exploration in the western provinces (see Figure 7:1, page 110). This exploration has been highly successful, particularly in the discovery of the Western Pembina field in Alberta and in the development of several formerly marginal shallow gas prospects. As a result, the oil industry has *re*-revised its estimates of Canadian petroleum reserves, particularly of natural gas, and is again pressuring the governments for increased exports. While estimates of low reserves have served their purpose in convincing the federal government to sponsor oil-industry profitability through high prices, the current phase of high reserves estimates is aimed at further increasing profitability and growth through expanded production for export.

Despite increased government involvement, then, the Canadian oil industry continues to strive to further its own economic self-interests and to befuddle its government partners and the public in the process. Before concluding with some policy recommendations about how the system could be improved, I would like to examine what the role of the oil companies could be in a more centrally regulated, but still capitalistically organized, petroleum industry in this country.

A NEW ROLE FOR THE OIL COMPANIES?

The central figures in this book, the oilmen of Calgary, are a privileged group within the Canadian social mosaic. Within the industry itself, they enjoy the best jobs, the highest incomes, and the most security, free from either the difficult manual work of those who actually encounter oil on drilling rigs, rural production sites, or as workers in refineries; or the boring routine of the phalanx of female secretaries in service to the oilmen. The oilmen themselves comprise two social classes, both within the industry and within Canadian society. Most of them—the professional workers, technical experts, junior- and middle-level managers, and small capitalist entrepreneurs—are solidly middle class. A smaller number—the few entrepreneurs who strike it rich through a favourable land position or successful wildcat well, and the senior executives of the large oil companies—comprise the upper class of the industry. Either directly, or through converting their position and high salaries into large holdings of corporate stocks and other investments, they become major owners of private property. In a capitalist system, this is their entry ticket into the economic elite of Canadian society, the propertied rich.

The middle-class oilmen do not resent the more privileged few. Enjoying comfortable life styles themselves, they view such success as the just reward of those who work the hardest, risk the most, and thereby contribute most to the viability of their industry. The middle-class oilmen are either reconciled to their own level or see the upper echelons as the goal to which they strive in their own careers. The legitimacy of the system as a whole, with its attendant inequalities of position and wealth, is accepted without question.

This same unquestioning attitude is taken towards the role of the Albertan oil industry in Canadian society as a whole. While the formation of oil and natural gas and its geographical location was an entirely impersonal, prehistoric process, the oilmen choose not to give much credit to this nonhuman fact. Instead, the good fortune that petroleum has bestowed upon the people of Alberta and, in particular, the oilmen of Calgary is attributed to the oil industry itself. The foreign-owned oil industry with its hard working oilmen is credited for the good fortune that Alberta enjoys. The son of the Albertan farmer who is now a well-paid petroleum engineer for a Canadian major attributes his success to his own hard work and drive; he blames the unemployed Atlantic fisherman's son for his poverty and dependency upon "the Canadian taxpayer" (meaning, primarily, the Calgary oilman).

There is, of course, something to be said for the oilman's view. He deserves credit for taking advantage of his opportunity. But, he unconsciously chooses to attribute the results of a complex interplay of biochemical, geophysical, geographical, historical, social, *and* personal processes to the last of these alone. The free-enterprise myth conveniently sustains this self-serving view.

On the world scene in recent years, petroleum politics and economics have altered dramatically; and the role of the major oil companies has altered flexibly to adapt to the changing conditions. Oil companies now market state-owned South American crude, explore for new reserves on a contract basis with European governments in the North Sea, and even build shopping complexes for Arabian sheiks. The role of the companies has altered appreciably in Canada as well. They no longer run the country's petroleum show on their own terms in their own way. They have not been eclipsed, but have entered a new phase where they are implicitly allied wth the federal government and the governments of the producing provinces. None of these changes, however, has been sought by the oilmen. They have resisted "interference" bitterly, and have adapted—profitably adapted—only as they have had to. To the extent that they have an industry strategy for dealing with governments, the oilmen's can be summed up as *resistance followed by rapid adaptation*. When change is imposed, they can be heard to utter their cliche: "We don't like it, but we can live with it."

In times like these, when Canada faces grave and far-reaching decisions on energy policies, the monotonous persistence with which the oilmen stick to their free-enterprise line is depressing. I recently asked the president of a wholly owned Canadian major what he foresaw for the future of Canadian energy policy and the role of the major oil companies. His reply: "I sincerely hope that the *status quo* is held."

Perhaps the structural constraints of competitive capitalism are too great to expect oilmen to behave any differently, and the cultural constraints of the free-enterprise myth too great to expect them to think differently. If the structural and cultural conditions were altered, along the lines I will suggest in the next section, however, the oilmen would have to adopt a wider vision and transform their role to better serve Canada's interests (while still maintaining profitable enterprise).

The first requirement would be that the nature of the oil companies themselves be demystified, not only for outsiders but for oilmen as well. The oil companies are neither the all-powerful evil-doers depicted by some critics, nor are they the incomprehensible but essential organizations that oilmen like to proclaim. As one informed outside commentator has put it: "It is difficult, as it has always been difficult, to see the big companies for what they are, to look through the emperor's clothes.... they are simply trading companies with shifting allegiances whose overriding aim is to make money.... they have been basically committees of engineers and accountants preoccupied like most businessmen with profit margins, safeguarding investments and avoiding taxation" (Sampson, 1975:309).

What can such companies offer the Canadian people today? The analyses of this study suggest that they can offer a means to explore for, develop, transport, refine, and market Canadian petroleum reserves through the efficient and flexible mobilization of capital, technology, expertise, and trained manpower. Other means could be devised for achieving these ends but, at the moment, this is the best—indeed the only—means at our disposal. But the oil companies' position should be viewed as one of privilege that entails serious social responsibilities on their part. I am not referring to corporate responsibility in the public-relations sense, but to a new conception of the social contract between private companies and the public governments that represent the people of a nation. The companies should come to view their position as a privileged one that has to be protected by a long-term concern for societal problems, not exploited by a narrow pursuit of short-term economic self-interest. Their present course may lead eventually to expropriation, nationalization, and the realization of all the rest of the oilmen's worst fears; not because people and governments do not understand the industry, but because they come to feel justifiably that they have to protect themselves from it.

What could such a socially informed and concerned role for the oil companies entail? It would have to start with a sensitivity about social as well as economic needs and an attempt to mesh company proposals with national and provincial priorities. Take, for example, the exploration and development of the petroleum reserves offshore Newfoundland and Labrador. According to the old, free-enterprise mentality, reserves off that province are no different from reserves anywhere else, except in terms of the different technological problems and economics involved in their exploitation. The government of that province should (as a senior executive at Imperial advised me) let the companies in to develop the reserves as rapidly as possible, and simply collect its royalties. The Imperial official was insensitive to the way in which such a policy could disrupt viable local economies and the fishing industry, upset established social and cultural patterns, leave an unskilled labour force still unskilled, and even create new problems through the massive increase in government revenues themselves.

Within a restructured Canadian petroleum industry, the oil companies could take a different approach. They would first have to become informed about the province and its problems, then try to devise a strategy for development that took local needs into account. This, of course, would have to be done in close consultation with the provincial and federal government. A company could offer a kind of package contract which might include the provision of infrastructure for towns that were to become exploration and production centres, training and apprenticeship programs for local workers, and compensation payments to groups such as native Indians and Inuit who would be inconvenienced by the development. In return, the company would be granted the right to develop the resource for a fair rate of return. Companies that took the lead in initiating such an approach would have the added advantage of getting a head start on their competitors.

Currently, the oil industry, even in Canada, is gradually evolving towards a position in which the companies will be working on a contract basis for governments; therefore, the companies' behaviour will be closely regulated and the information they produce will be publicly accountable. This is not undue interference in the free-enterprise system, but rather the only terms under which a modern society can afford to have its resources developed by private enterprise. To date, the oilmen have chosen to resist the trend at each step. They have had to be bludgeoned into it by provincial and national governments intent upon gaining control, but lacking the experience and expertise to avoid costly mistakes in the process. How much better it would be if the oilmen could enter into the changing scene progressively and creatively. To do so could be to contribute significantly, in new ways, to Canada's energy future and the social and economic development of its diverse regions. To fail to do so could be to hasten the decline of the vital community and way of life that oilmen hold so dearly.

As the Canadian oil industry is presently constituted, the above discussion undoubtedly presents a rather romantic and utopian view of the capitalist oil companies. I have shown earlier how the competitive constraints of the system impose the profit and growth motives as major priorities, whatever the personal sentiments of oilmen. On the other hand, I do believe that some oilmen would be sympathetic to such a change if it were practically feasible. Perhaps it is symptomatic that Robert Blair, president of Alberta Gas Trunk Line Co. Ltd. (AGTL) and the engineer of its dramatic takeover of 35 per cent of the shares of Husky Oil despite the contrary bidding of both Occidental Petroleum Corporation and Petro-Canada, has noted "with some pride" that his share purchase probably reduced U.S. ownership of Husky from 80 per cent to about 40 per cent and referred to AGTL's "emotional commitment to the lessening of foreign ownership of petroleum companies in Canada" (*Maclean's*, July 10, 1978: 50–51).

The responsibility of government agencies and of realistic critical commentators, within this context of carving out a new role for the oil companies, is to reconstitute the organization of the industry so that the companies would choose to channel their energy and efficiency more directly and consistently to serve the public interest. Given the present political climate, it would be more realistic for left-wing and liberal critics to push for a more regulated capitalist oil industry than to continue to view public ownership and nationalization as a panacea. I will conclude by considering the kinds of policies that might make it possible to move towards a centrally controlled but decentrally organized petroleum industry in Canada.

CONCLUSION: SOME POLICY CONSIDERATIONS

I have suggested that Canadian oil policy is now effectively being formulated by the Canadian majors in concert with the federal and Albertan governments. This policy includes charging extremely high prices for our remaining conventional reserves of crude oil in the western provinces, prices that bear no relation whatever to the costs of producing those reserves (about sixty-eight cents a barrel). The lion's share of the immense revenues created goes to the governments of the producing provinces, mainly Alberta. This is Alberta's windfall reward for happening to be sitting atop the country's major oil and gas fields at a time when other people's initiative in a distant part of the world, the Middle East, has effected a radical increase in the price of crude oil in world markets. The high price is thereby a mechanism for transferring wealth from the consuming to the producing provinces. A second share of the revenue generated goes to the federal government in the form of income tax. The rest is profit to the oil companies.[15]

The rationale for high prices is given by the other two strands of current Canadian energy policy: its goal and the means to achieving it. The goal is energy self-reliance through rapid exploration and development; the means to achieving it is through stimulating private enterprise to do the job with their new, higher profits.

The critics are wrong, then, in suggesting that Canada lacks an energy policy. It has a policy but it is not, and cannot be, as clearly stated as it might be under a public-enterprise system. The critics are surely right, however, in questioning the wisdom of that policy.

The first question has to do with macroeconomics. In a national economy which already depends heavily upon raw material extraction and primary industry, how much of the nation's resources of capital, technology, expertise, and manpower should be devoted to a strategy that will surely further the economy's imbalance? If my analysis of the international energy picture above is correct, the OPEC countries will continue to provide an expensive supply of crude oil for the consuming nations, although we can expect periodic disruptions in that supply. Canada need not commit itself to a policy of energy self-reliance out of panic. A sophisticated, long-term cost-benefit analysis of alternative strategies is needed.

The problem of economic imbalance is compounded in two ways by the mechanism of higher prices through which the goal of self-reliance in energy is to be achieved. First, Canadian manufacturing already suffers competitive disadvantages through a restricted local market, high wages coupled with low productivity, and the branch-plant nature of many of its operations. Cheap oil and gas could make this sector more competitive; expensive energy puts it at a worse disadvantage. Second, since most of the Canadian oil producers are foreign owned, a large share—perhaps more than half—of the companies' windfall profits will be appropriated from Canada by the foreign parents. These profits will be used not for Canadian exploration, but for further enriching American and European shareholders and for financing the international expansion of the major oil companies. In addition, there is no guarantee that the share of profits retained by the subsidiaries for reinvestment will be used in the way government policy-makers envisage. In 1977, despite high profits, the Canadian oil industry involved itself in an effective investment strike against the government of Newfoundland and Labrador over offshore exploration. And it has been pursuing a continuing "go-slow" action against the federal government over northern exploration. For the industry, high profits today are not enough; it demands the guarantee of high profits and stability tomorrow as well. The chronic dilemma of governments that rely upon the private-enterprise system is that they must capitulate to such demands if they want to meet their economic objectives.

There is no simple solution to this dilemma. I have suggested that outright nationalization and the creation of a state-run oil industry could create as many problems as it could solve. What is required, instead, is a vigorous policy aimed at improving the various governments' bargaining power with the companies. This involves much greater, not less, government regulation of and involvement in the industry. The piecemeal progress towards increased government involvement should be pursued more consciously. Policy-makers should concentrate on four main elements: repatriation, information control, direct involvement, and direct regulation.

Repatriation is not simply an emotional issue, nor is it only a problem of economic surplus. In the present context, it has to do with bargaining power, an aspect of sovereignty. The Canadian majors are much less dependent upon their Canadian assets than they would be without their multinational status. With parental approval and backing, they can resist government pressure to conform to its policies. Conversely, governments are in a relatively strong bargaining position when dealing with non-affiliated companies dependent upon their Canadian assets. Repatriation could be effected through a variety of means which might include: some public ownership, participation agreements, mandatory share issues to Canadian citizens, and expanded employee-participation schemes. Employee participation that went beyond ownership to include some decision-making might even contribute to democratizing the Canadian oil industry. Such schemes could be effected if the political will were there.

The ways in which the industry's control and manipulation of crucial information are central to its bargaining power with governments have already been discussed. This monopoly power should be decisively broken. Government agencies need to have complete access to all company information about estimated reserves, exploration and production plans, capitalization and financing. Such information is vital if governments are to formulate intelligent energy policies and to distinguish fact from fiction when negotiating with the oil companies. The current level of corporate secrecy is politically and morally untenable. Wholly owned Canadian subsidiaries do not even have to produce an annual report. Such reports are in any case highly unreliable and almost a joke among corporate officers and accounting firms. Governments should appoint their own auditors, who should be financially independent of the firms they investigate. Such policies would no doubt be wildly unpopular with oilmen.

At present, governments often have no choice but to capitulate to industry demands because if private enterprise fails to do a job it will not get done. To counter this, governments should become more directly involved in the oil industry, not simply as marketing agencies or as exploration companies for facilitating private-enterprise efforts, but as full-fledged oil companies. The surest and quickest way to accomplish this would be to buy majority control in a large, fully integrated

American-owned Canadian major: say, Imperial Oil, Gulf, or Texaco.[16] (The choice would depend upon financial considerations and preliminary negotiations.) This proposal sounds more radical than it is, as the change could be implemented with little effect upon corporate structure. Such a purchase would also further the other policy objectives I have been discussing. In the longer term, governments could aim towards achieving a greater involvement in the industry, say thirty per cent. Such public companies should have to meet the same efficiency criteria as the private firms. The public companies, however, would return their profits to the public purse rather than to wealthy (mainly foreign) citizens and would be an invaluable source of government information for controlling the industry.

Governments should be moving towards what I have termed "direct regulation" of the oil industry. This is an explicit compromise between state-run enterprise on a large scale and what we have now—that is, indirect regulation through price manipulation, exploration incentives, depletion allowances, and so on. Governments should abandon the feeble efforts they are making to get the oil companies to co-operate and, instead, set up their own exploration and production programs and hire the oil companies on a contract basis to carry out the work. This would allow both centralized planning and decentralized, competitive enterprise. In addition, the kinds of bureaucratic weaknesses that have plagued the Soviet petroleum industry could be avoided.

It is also important to consider the social impact of any energy policy. The policy implicitly adopted by the triumvirate of oil companies, federal government, and western producing provinces essentially calls for rapid expansion. This policy suits the oil companies' collective drive towards growth and increased profits. However, the long-term effects of such a policy upon Canadian society could be harmful. As a rough but not inaccurate generalization, we can predict that a rapid rate of petroleum exploration and development will reinforce current economic trends in Canada and speed up the disruption of the ecology and the social and cultural fabric of the areas of Canada directly affected: northern Alberta and British Columbia, the Mackenzie Delta, the Arctic islands, and coastal Newfoundland and Labrador.

In each of these areas, the local economies (the bases of

local social and cultural life) are almost totally unsuited for and unprepared for massive industrialization. If the federal government were concerned to protect and strengthen the pluralism and diversity of the Canadian heritage, the first policy priority should be the improvement of these local economies. Paradoxically, Canada's present energy strategy could weaken these economies even further. The prospect of the industrial development of the frontier is usually sold to local people and their advocates on the basis of the jobs and business opportunities it will create. Such an argument makes sense and has some validity in terms of a market mentality. But it misses the broader sociological point. If such a policy is pursued rapidly and insensitively, local populations are incorporated into the national industrial system as unskilled and semi-skilled workers— that is, they become a proletariat in the Marxist sense. As a corollary to this process, other viable or potentially viable forms of economic organization, such as independent commodity production, are either severely disrupted or entirely destroyed (Hedley, 1976). In allowing the metropolitan regions to expropriate the energy resources located in the hinterland in such an ill-considered way, the government would perpetuate and exacerbate Canada's severe regional disparities.

This is not to say that I believe in some romantic ideal of the simple life as lived in an independent frontier community. The reality is much more complex than that and does not justify, in my opinion, an anti-industrial stance. Nevertheless, it is true to say that the current energy policy has not been thought through carefully enough and its long-term implications for the future of Canadian society have been all but ignored.[17] Far preferable would be a slower, more controlled program of development, co-ordinated with complementary measures for strengthening local economies, and explicitly aimed towards preserving Canada's ethnic, cultural, and regional diversity. Such a policy would mean a much more subdued (but still vital) role for Canadian oil companies.

Postscript 1979

The perceived "crisis" in the oil industry during the mid-1970s has passed: the oilmen of Calgary have emerged victorious from their confrontation with the federal and provincial governments. The oilmen have become the leading figures in the triumvirate that determines Canadian oil policy. In the words of one prominent oilman: "We are at a period of growth and expansion in western Canada unparalleled in the history of the petroleum industry. [Incentives will be continued] because the provinces have learned their lesson" (W. W. Siebens quoted in *Oilweek*, December 19, 1977, p. 13). This is confirmed from governments' side. A high-ranking official of Saskatchewan's Department of Mineral Resources confessed to me lately: "We had to learn that profits is not a dirty word." The federal government has accepted the oil companies' demands that Canadian crude-oil prices move towards the world level and that prices for synthetic crude from the Alberta oil sands be at world levels. We can expect that the oil companies will press for and get a similar concession for oil and gas produced from the northern and east-coast offshore frontiers. As these new sources constitute a larger share of domestically produced petroleum, the average price of Canadian oil will rise accordingly.

In addition, the industry's investment strike of 1974 and 1975 has succeeded in convincing governments to play the facilitative role expected of them by the industry—to provide generous exploration incentives in the form of tax concessions and depletion allowances, and to allow the establishment of Canadian drilling funds through which wealthy individuals and groups can enjoy 100 per cent tax write-offs for money invested in petroleum exploration. The most notable depletion allowance is the federal government's "super depletion" for wells costing over $5 million. In effect, the majors are subsidized through lost tax revenue up to ninety cents out of every dollar they spend on these expensive exploration wells in the frontier regions. I want to emphasize that we are now further than ever from a system of *free* enterprise. The Canadian oil industry works through private enterprise heavily subsidized by the public through high prices and tax concessions. The government-administered monopoly prices also provide for massive royalty incomes to the producing provinces, particularly Alberta. The industry has become more highly regulated during the past decade, but this is experienced by the companies as more of a nuisance than a basic change in how the system works.

Canada's industry-sponsored oil policies have the full support of the four western provinces which are currently enjoying an exploration boom, as well as the support of Nova Scotia and Newfoundland which hope that high prices and super depletion will make them into oil-producing regions, while Quebec's strong stand on provincial control over natural resources locks it into supporting Alberta despite the difficulties for its own consumers. Ontario has become isolated as a voice crying in the wind in its plea for restraint. It has argued—reasonably, I think—that the arbitrary OPEC price is not (as Alberta's Premier Lougheed likes to maintain) a true market price, and is therefore not the basis on which Canadian oil policy should be based. Ontario is worried by the erosion of its manufacturing, owing to increased international competition and economic recession, and argues that less expensive energy costs can help offset these other pressures. Although clearly self-interested, its arguments may nevertheless be correct for the national interest. Why has the federal government, under both Liberal and Progressive Conservative leadership, chosen to give more weight to the oil companies and to the producing provinces?

There are two main reasons: the first reason is structural; the second, moral in the broad sense of that term. The first is the more important. The government has come to recognize, as never before, its dependency upon the private oil companies (mainly foreign-owned but the same logic applies to domestic companies). If it does not have to capitulate completely to the companies (as it has not done, for example, on the issue of oil exports to the U.S.), it does have to concede enough to guarantee generous profits and stimulation for new exploration. Otherwise, the oil companies have made it clear that they will refuse to contribute the exploration and development effort to which the federal government has committed itself in its goal of energy self-reliance. The only alternative—which would take a long time to put in place and would have its own growing pains—would be to substitute public for private enterprise in the Canadian petroleum industry. Not only would there be practical difficulties in making this switch in the short- and medium-term, but the Liberal and Progressive-Conservative parties are morally and ideologically committed to private enterprise. This brings us to the interesting question of the role of the national oil company, Petro-Canada.

Since its establishment by the former Liberal government, Petro-Canada has grown remarkably quickly to become a major force on the Canadian petroleum scene. Through buying the Canadian subsidiaries of two large American companies (Arco and Pacific Petroleum), it has become one of the top ten producing companies in the country. This has provided some cash flow for supporting what it considers to be its main purposes, the stimulation of frontier exploration and the production of non-conventional crude and heavy oils. In this, it is not at cross-purposes with the privately owned oil industry. Instead, it has been acting as a catalyst for joint-venture operations that the private companies might not risk on their own initiative. Contrary to industry propaganda, the public company has been taking the most risks. And this has benefited the Canadian majors by allowing them to participate in potentially profitable exploration and development opportunities that they would not otherwise risk. Specifically, Petro-Canada has: begun establishing a large research centre in Calgary to focus upon Canadian energy problems; investigated Arctic transportation possibilities for liquified natural gas; participated in heavy-oil development in the Lloydminster region in Saskatchewan; negotiated as a potential importer for the federal government in direct dealings with the national oil companies of Mexico and Venezuela; increased the Canadian share of the ownership and control of our petroleum industry; and stimulated frontier exploration by participating in no fewer than 47 of the 97 frontier wells drilled by the industry between 1971 and 1978 (*Financial Post*, May 26, 1979, p. 1). Even the ultraconservative editorial line of *Oilweek* has given grudging appreciation to Petro-Canada, suggesting that "it would be pushing the clock backward if Canada disbanded Petro-Canada" (June 18, 1979, p. 3).

Despite its impressive record, the new Progressive-Conservative Prime Minister is currently insisting that he intends to remove Petro-Canada's exploration advantages and to sell off the profitable parts of its operations to private interests. His reasoning exemplifies the moral dimension of our government's commitment to the oil companies. Mr. Clark has been quoted as saying: "We do not want an oil company run like the Post Office" (*Oilweek*, May 14, 1979, p. 52). What he has failed to realize, however, is that it is not public *versus* private enterprise that is crucial, but rather the structural conditions in which the companies operate. As my earlier analysis suggests, these conditions encourage efficiency and flexibility within the Canadian oil industry, and they affect Petro-Canada in the same way as they do any other oil company (including other government-owned companies such as BP Canada). Petro-Canada's working environment is totally different from that of the Canadian post office and this difference, rather than the composition of its board of directors, is crucial. If there is one clear policy implication of this book, it is that energy decisions for Canada should be based upon a pragmatic understanding of how each energy sector works, rather than upon ideological commitment to free enterprise (or, for that matter, state enterprise). From this pragmatic perspective, Petro-Canada would appear to have a crucial and expanding role to play.

Although they have had to make some concessions, as in agreeing to phase out oil exports and to accept a price for conventional crude below the OPEC level, the oil companies with their free-enterprise ideology have successfully reconfirmed their ascendancy on the Canadian oil scene. Federal and provincial governments have agreed to support profitable private enterprise as the means to providing a secure energy future for Canadians. But how well has this sytem with its attendant policy been working during the past five years? I have suggested that high prices and tax incentives are blunt instruments for stimulating petroleum exploration, and this impression is supported by the evidence. As the oilmen predicted, exploration activity has increased dramatically since the "climate for investment" (higher prices and more incentives) changed in their favour. But the *pattern* of this increased exploration has not been the one hoped for by the federal government. While 1977, 1978, and 1979 have been banner years for the western oil industry with record levels of land sales, geophysical activity, and drilling, frontier exploration in the Mackenzie Delta, the Beaufort Sea, the Arctic islands, and the high Arctic has continued to decline. The government's target, as set out in *An Energy Strategy for Canada* (1976), was to *double* exploration activity in the frontiers in the subsequent three years. Instead, exploration has *dropped* by two-thirds (*Financial Post*, May 26, 1979, p. 19). It is noteworthy that it is being kept alive mainly by three Canadian companies: Petro-Canada, Panarctic, and Dome Petroleum. In the north, the investment strike continues. Miffed by the Berger inquiry, the oil companies are holding out for assured pipeline and/or tanker transportation systems, for higher prices, and for access to large markets (mainly the U.S.) before they will resume large-scale exploration. We can expect to see federal concessions in each of these areas during the next decade. Its commitment to the present system of industry organization gives the government no choice. (Alternatively, it *could* achieve greater leverage by hiring companies directly on a contract basis, or by expanding direct public involvement in petroleum exploration.)

The east-coast offshore, due largely to super depletion (which is scheduled to expire in 1980) and to the readiness of the government of Newfoundland to issue wide-ranging exploration permits once it won a victory in principle over the oil companies for offshore jurisdiction, has seen a great deal of drilling activity in 1979. A major discovery, particularly of oil, may lead to further increases in 1980; but talk of Newfoundland's becoming a great oil- and gas-producing centre are premature at present. More than ever, the province of Alberta, more specifically the cities of Edmonton and Calgary, are the established energy centres of the country.

The position of Calgary within the Canadian mosaic has altered dramatically since the early 1970s. No longer a hinterland, it is now firmly established as a metroplitan centre in its own right. Major oil firms such as Imperial and Texaco have established separate resource companies with their head offices in Calgary; Imperial has shifted several senior executives from

Toronto to its western headquarters. This is not decentralization, but a recognition of Calgary as the centre of the companies' energy-resource activities. The relationship with the rest
of the country is illustrated by the mode of east-coast offshore
operations. Rather than move permanently to Halifax or St.
John's, managerial and professional oilmen take up temporary
residence for the drilling season or even commute on a two-
weeks-on, two-weeks-off basis. The few executives who are
asked to settle more permanently enjoy "compensations" such
as salary bonuses and company houses.

The new oil boom has triggered a real-estate boom in Calgary, with new office complexes being constructed at dizzying
speeds. The skyline is unrecognizable from just a decade ago.
The changes reflect more than just new riches, but also a real
shift in economic power to the west. Calgary is rapidly becoming a *financial* centre in its own right. The Alberta stock exchange is expanding and the westward shift is symbolized by
the Bank of Montreal's recent decision to move the chairman
of its board to Calgary.

But what of the oilmen of Calgary? My contention in the
concluding chapter that they would have to adapt to a new,
more liberal regime for their own self-preservation has proved
wrong. Owing to governments' structural dependency upon
them and to the new conservatism among Western nations,
the oilmen's established views and ways of doing things have
regained ascendancy. The oil community's crisis and critical
self-examination is over. Not only are they secure once again
in their social world, but they have also become a more powerful and important part of Canadian society. These men—and
others of their ilk in national and foreign corporate head offices—with the beliefs, prejudices, satisfactions, dissatisfactions,
and career aspirations as described in this book, promise to
continue as the chief architects of Canada's energy future for
the rest of this century.

Appendix I
Methodology: Studying the Oil Industry

The research upon which this analysis has been based was guided by two general principles. First, it was based on a realist and humanist rather than a positivist philosophy of science (Harré, 1960, 1972; House, 1975, 1976; Keat and Urry, 1975; Ryan, 1970). Second, it took a discovery-oriented rather than a testing-oriented approach to sociological investigation (Glaser and Strauss, 1967). These two principles are interrelated, and I will discuss them together.

The positivist philosophy of science holds that the fundamental aim of science is to discover universal regularities. These natural laws can then be expressed in terms of formalized deductive systems (theories) and, together with specific empirical propositions, can be used to deduce specific empirical facts and, more importantly, new universal laws (Homans, 1974; Merton, 1948; Rudner, 1966). Once a science has reached maturity, research should be governed by established theories, and should seek to test the validity of those theories. Where a theory or part of a theory fails to stand up to empirical testing, it has been falsified, and must therefore be abandoned or modified (Popper, 1959). Ideally, then, research becomes a process of testing known theories, so that they can be modified and our knowledge of the world improved.

Recently, the positivist model of science has come under attack for failing to portray accurately what scientists actually do (Krohn, 1974; Kuhn, 1962). Without entering into that academic debate, it is enough to note for present purposes that the realist philosophy of science provides a rather different model which renders many of the critics' objections immaterial. The realist asserts that, although the quest for wide-ranging empirical generalizations (a softened version of the positivist's natural laws) is important, it is not the core of scientific practice. That, instead, is the attempt to describe accurately states, processes, and relations among phenomena conceived as systems, and to discover and, where necessary, construct imaginatively the underlying causal mechanisms or systems that explain those observable states, processes, and relations. The term "underlying" should be understood metaphorically as referring to some causal system which is not itself obvious or easily observable. Examples of such theories in the natural sciences are the atomic theory of matter, the virus theory of disease, and the Darwinian theory of evolution. Examples in the social sciences are Marx's theory of capitalism, Durkheim's sociological theory of religion, Freud's theory of personality, and C. Wright Mills's theory of the power elite. These examples suggest that theories in the social sciences are of two types: the universal and the historically specific. The first are assumed to apply to all human societies (Durkheim and Freud), the second only to specific historical periods and places (Marx and Mills). Because societies continually change over time, historically specific theories are more important in social than natural science.

This view of the nature of scientific theory and explanation suggests a different role for research than does the positivist model. Rather than being confined to testing known theories, research becomes an important part of the process of discovering theories and, equally importantly, the main activity for developing accurate descriptions of the empirical world that require theoretical explanation. This is particularly true for social science, since the empirical systems themselves are continually changing. The first prerequisite for good theorizing is accurate description of empirical reality. Theorizing should be guided by good research.[1]

I believe that the positivist philosophy of science has led the bulk of sociological research into wrong directions for a very long time. Despite a tremendous proliferation of journals and textbooks and the development of many sophisticated research and statistical techniques, our knowledge about the core institutions of society remains woefully inadequate; and even sociologists turn to others—journalists, statesmen, social critics, popular writers—for many facts and ideas about how their society really works. The field of economic sociology is particularly underdeveloped. Where is our sociology of the stock market? Of bond traders? Of bankers? Of real estate developers?

Of farmers? Of small businessmen? Of multinational corpora-
tons? Of the steel industry? Of fisheries? and so forth. Sociology remains all but mute on these topics, which are surely
crucial to any attempt to understand our society. Even when
they are dealt with, it is more by accident than by design—e.g.,
someone wants to study informal processes within complex
organizations and happens to choose an automobile factory;
but it could as easily have been a school or a hospital.

The sociological imagination, which surely would be interested in the factory for its own sake, and for how it ties into
economic and social life in a contemporary capitalist society,
has been stultified by the positivist recipe for theory-controlled,
testing-oriented research. Nor is the problem confined to so-
called straight or mainstream sociology. As indicated in the
preceding chapter, radical and critical sociologists, while at
least focusing upon core institutions of society, also fail either
to ground their theories in their research or to contribute much
in the way of fresh descriptions about social and economic life.

This is not to suggest that theory in the grand sense—that is,
a theory of the nature and future direction of our society—is
unimportant. On the contrary, it is crucial. But it needs to be
complemented by a new concern for accurate, empirical descriptions of various sectors of our social system—not just
micro-level descriptions of small groups but of important industries, government bureaucracies, public services, and so on.
After 100 years of sociology, we still lack a detailed ethnography of our own society. Such an ethnography would surely
make for better-informed theorizing and policy-making.

It was in this spirit that the investigation reported here was
conceived and conducted. It has, admittedly, focused more
upon the purely descriptive than the theory-generating function of research, although I have tried to deal with some of the
theoretical implications for understanding contemporary capitalism in the concluding chapter, and in an earlier article
(House, 1977a). In addition to following the realist philosophy
of science, I have also attempted to step outside the boundaries
of science to try to understand the psychology of Calgary
oilmen. Sociology should, I think, avowedly and explicitly recognize itself as a hybrid discipline between the sciences and the
humanities (Berger, 1963). There is no contradiction in this.
My concern has been not only to describe and explain in a

scientific sense, but also to understand a community of human beings with their own characteristic strengths and weaknesses, satisfactions and dissatisfactions. Oilmen represent a social and psychological type poorly understood by others in society, particularly those of us who like to think of ourselves as academic and intellectual. The quotation from E. M. Forster's *Howards End* at the beginning of this book is a literary attempt to deal with the same subject, and neatly captures the humanistic theme of my analysis.

One of the striking features of the research, on a more mundane level, was the methodological problems, in the narrow sense,[2] that it entailed. The conventional textbooks are mute about how one goes about studying an industry or a multinational corporation. And critical sociologists rely almost entirely upon secondary sources of data and upon the imaginative reconstruction of the economic and social process that they suppose must underlie the data. But it was those processes themselves and the people involved in them that we were interested in.[3] How does one study those?

If one wants to develop an ethnography of a social system as a whole, the ideal method, as practised by anthropologists and some sociologists, is participant observation. But this method is limited to small social systems. It would take years to investigate the Calgary-based operations of even a single major oil company by this method. The conventional sociological survey method, on the other hand, although suited to large populations, is designed for studying not social systems but the social characteristics of individuals and aggregates that are members of such systems. A testing-oriented method, it is ill-suited to the open, probing, discovery-oriented approach we needed.

Perhaps the most flexible of sociological methods is the personal interview. It can be structured or open-ended, short or long. It can be used with people in different social positions and in a variety of situations. It has much greater scope than participant observation, allows for the kind of exploratory investigation that surveys preclude, and provides the personal contact that is impossible with either a survey or an analysis of secondary data sources. For these reasons, the personal interview became our main investigative tool.

Of course, the personal interview also has its short-comings. It is more superficial than participant observation, and one can never be sure that interviewees are being honest in their answers, or even that one is asking the right questions. We attempted, therefore, to complement interviewing by participant observation where possible. This proved to be a productive method, but I was unable to arrange as much direct observation as I had hoped. There is also a limit to the number of people who can be interviewed, and it proved difficult to ensure that our sample of interviewees was truly representative of the Calgary oil community. Though important, representativeness was not our main concern in the interviews. We wanted to talk to people who could tell us as much as possible about the oil industry in Calgary, and at the same time to ensure that we included a cross-section of occupations and companies. To deal with the problem of representativeness and to get systematic data for a large number of oilmen, we decided to conduct a survey as well. The aim of the survey, however, was somewhat different from that of conventional methodology. It was conceived as part of the discovery-oriented process and used to check out some of the initial impressions from interviews, to give more systematic data, and to provide additional information on some topics.

Finally, the danger that the investigator would become so caught up in the world he was investigating that he would fail to see the woods for the trees had to be guarded against. Secondary data sources and secondary commentary upon the international and the national oil scenes were used to set the present study in context and to provide a wider perspective upon the Calgary oil community than its members themselves could be expected to have.

This rather mixed methodology is a far from perfect instrument, and we feel that, theoretically, there should be a better, tidier way. Practically, however, we do not know what that way might have been. Part of the challenge of doing this type of sociology is to try to develop better techniques in the future. I will now describe each of the methods used in more detail.

PERSONAL INTERVIEWS

In organizing the personal interviews, we tried to balance three objectives: to sample a cross-section of people in different companies and positions within the industry, to try to acquire a detailed knowledge of the operations of a major oil company, and to include people with long experience in the industry who could provide good information. To develop our picture of the industry as a whole, therefore, we decided upon an informal stratified sampling technique and supplemented this with a snowball technique in which we asked the interviewees for leads to key informants. For the in-depth part of the research, we chose Imperial Oil Limited because it is the largest and most powerful Canadian oil company, and because we already had an initial entree through Imperial's provision of some no-strings-attached financing for the project. I myself, as principal investigator, carried out all the interviews at Imperial; most of the other interviewing was done by three research assistants.

In all, we conducted 124 personal interviews: fifty-five at Imperial, twenty at other large oil companies (including all the Canadian majors and large independents), twenty-five at small companies, five at drilling companies, eight at service companies, four with consultants, two with senior officers of the Canadian Petroleum Association, two with senior officers of the Independent Petroleum Association of Canada, one with an officer of the Alberta Energy Resources Conservation Board, and two with former employees who had quit the industry. At Imperial, I interviewed twenty-one members of the Production Department (including six of its eight senior-level managers based in Calgary); twenty-seven members of the Exploration Department (including nine of ten top-level local managers); three senior managers at the Toronto head office (the Chairman of the Board and Chief Executive Officer, the Vice-President in charge of Production, and the Manager of Business Development); the Western Regional manager; the manager of Employee Relations; the General Services manager; and a member of the Legal Department. The non-managerial engineers, geologists, and geophysicists interviewed represented approximately a 10 per cent sample. I chose the names more or less at random from lists provided by the company, but did try to include people from a variety of positions, levels, and exploration and production areas. Within the Exploration Department, however, a senior manager made the initial contact with the potential interviewees and in some cases made substitutions when someone was out of town, ill, or unwilling to be interviewed. This may have biased the sample somewhat towards those favourable to the company, although I did talk to some people in both departments who were quite critical of Imperial and dissatisfied with their jobs. On the whole, the refusal rate was extremely low, and this was true for all sectors of the industry. Most oilmen were willing, indeed eager, to have a chance to express their views.

To broaden our picture of the dominant corporate sector of the industry, and to get some feeling for how legitimately we could generalize from Imperial to the other majors, we interviewed representatives of all the other large Canadian producers and explorers. We tried to arrange the interviews with senior-line officers as far as possible, and were largely successful. We interviewed three presidents, three vice-presidents, seven other senior-line officers, four employee-relations managers, and three public-relations representatives.

Our sample of small oil companies was initially drawn from Nickle's *Canadian Oil Register* roughly at random, and this was supplemented by leads from the first interviewees to other "characters" and long-standing Calgary oilmen. We also tried to include interviews with members of Calgary's famous oil families—those who had established large family fortunes in the early Turner Valley days or after Leduc. We had some success in this, but not as much as we had hoped. Some of the smallest companies, two- or three-person operations, turned out to be really deal-making consultants, oil companies in name only at that stage in their careers. Our samples of drilling companies, service companies, and consultants were drawn in a similar way as those from the small oil companies.

The format for the interviews was semi-structured and purposefully very flexible (see Appendix III). We organized interviews around a set of guiding questions, which were modified for particular informants depending upon their position in the industry. Some interviewees stuck close to the questions, but most interviews ranged over a variety of topics, many of which were not covered in our prepared questions. We encouraged this and, as we ourselves became more knowledgeable about the industry and comfortable about interviewing, the interviews became more informal and conversational. We also changed some of the prepared questions as we learned more about the industry and developed new, tentative hypotheses for further exploration. I believe that this flexible approach is to be preferred in discovery-oriented research. The interviews ranged from three-quarters of an hours to two and a half hours, the median time being between an hour and an hour and a half. Most of those interviewed agreed to allow the conversations to be taped after being assured that their identities would be kept confidential. We cannot tell whether taping inhibited them in any way. There was no discernible difference in the information provided in the non-taped interviews. Recording by tape does allow the interviewer to maintain eye contact and to carry on a normal conversation which is not possible when one is taking notes. Tape recording also has the great advantage of letting the principal investigator listen to all of the original interviews.

DIRECT OBSERVATION

Although I never became a participant observer in the strict sense, I was able to attend a few meetings at Imperial Oil, and to go on a couple of field trips to some of the company's production sites. These sessions proved invaluable, and I regret that I was unable to do more of this kind of research. Company officials, however, after co-operating to arrange for me to sit in on one or two department meetings, became somewhat reluctant to include me in any more. In general, the same pattern occurred with the interviews; in the beginning, officials were very helpful in arranging interviews but began to get somewhat worried and suspicious as the research, from their point of view, seemed to go on and on.[4] Certainly, there were areas about which they openly refused to provide me with information. They were particularly reluctant to provide financial details and news about their latest technological advances and future exploration plans. This reluctance was consistent with the company's general security precautions, and I do not think their secrecy on these matters affected the sociological analysis very much.[5]

I attended two meetings in the Production Department, one in the Exploration Department, and one in the Land Department. These were useful for observing the processes discussed in interviews. At the meetings, junior-level managers and engineers, geologists, and geophysicists were called in to present various proposals, discuss problems, and answer questions. One could see the corporate hierarchy in action and the status differences between managers and workers very clearly. The meetings were run openly, but smoothly and efficiently, with a minimum of small talk and time-wasting upon minor details.[6] I also went on two field trips to the company's production operations in Alberta. One of these, to Devon and Golden Spike, was quite extensive, and I spent a lot of time talking to the area superintendent and a number of non-professional workers. The contrast with the Calgary head office was striking, and reminded me dramatically that the oilmen of Calgary are the privileged sector of the industry within Alberta. I would have liked to have gone on more field trips, particularly to some northern and offshore exploration sites, but such visits were difficult to arrange and expensive, and I suspect they would have contributed more towards satisfying my own curiosity than to this particular research project.

THE SURVEY

The aims of the survey were to gather more systematic data about many of the topics covered in personal interviews by testing them out on a larger and presumably more representative sample of oilmen and, more generally, to expand our data base for describing and understanding the oil community in Calgary. We administered a pre-test questionnaire to fourteen knowledgeable oilmen, and made a few modifications based on those suggestions before sending out the final questionnaire (see Appendix IV).

THE SAMPLE

In drawing our sample, we had to use two population lists (*Henderson's Street Directory* and the *Association of Professional Engineers of Alberta Membership Register*) to ensure that the sample was large enough and that it included a large proportion of engineers, geologists, and geophysicists. The sample was roughly stratified by occupation, although we have no way of knowing the actual proportions of each group within the total population of Calgary oilmen. We wanted to be sure of including large numbers of professional workers, managers, and entrepreneurs, and we feel that our somewhat unsystematic approach was justified given the exploratory nature of the research. Each of the sources listed Calgary residents by address, occupation, and company worked for. We drew a 5 per cent sample from each source which gave a total of 536 individuals to whom questionnaires and covering letters were sent. After a week, we sent follow-up letters urging people to fill in and return the questionnaires. We eventually received 350 completed questionnaires for a response rate of 65.6 per cent. The respondents worked for 97 different petroleum companies, 51 per cent of them for the majors (see Table Ap.I:1).[7] We did not conduct a follow-up study of nonrespondents, so we cannot be sure about how well our final sample represents the industry. It is possible, for example, that Americans and other immigrants were more suspicious of the study than native Canadians, and our findings might overstate the Canadianization of the industry's personnel.

Of the final sample, 39 per cent were professional workers (engineers, geologists, and geophysicists) by position within their organization, 12 per cent were executives, 22 per cent were managers, 23 per cent were supervisors, and 3 per cent were technicians (see Table Ap. I: 2). Note that most of the executives and managers were engineers and geologists by occupation, confirming our impression of upward mobility through the line. Our sample also picked up some accountants, technologists, and various other oilmen (mainly non-professional supervisors). Although we have discussed several of the personal demographic characteristics of the sample at various points throughout the text, for ease of reference a more extensive summary is provided in Table Ap. I: 3.

THE SCALES

In addition to a lot of personal and company demographic information, the questionnaire collected data on various dimensions of oilmen's attitudes, beliefs, satisfactions, and feelings. The questionnaire items used were adapted from a number of sources, with minor modifications to make the items suitable for the sample of oilmen. This had the disadvantage of making direct comparisons to other occupational groups difficult but did ensure that the questions and scales were meaningful for the sample. We chose and adapted scales to measure oilmen's political beliefs, job satisfaction, and alienation, as well as various job-related characteristics like decision-making opportunity, formalization, achievement opportunity, job participation, and job involvement. On the basis of the earlier personal interviews, we expected to find that oilmen would score high on economic conservatism, high on job satisfaction, low on alienation, low on formalization; would show much involvement in and control over their jobs; and that job satisfaction would be determined mainly by job-related features rather than wider organizational or career-related concerns. To varying degrees all of these expectations were confirmed. The

TABLE AP. I:1   Characteristics of Companies Employing Respondents

Characteristic	Percentage of Respondents
Primary Interests (N = 337)	
Integrated	29
Exploration, Production, and Land	16
Exploration and Production	26
Exploration	18
Production	9
Others	2
Head Office (N = 337)	
Calgary	66
Canada	86
Company type (N = 342)	
Major	51
Independent	45
Consulting	2
Other	2
Size	
Number of Canada employees (N = 324)	
Under 250	26
250 – 500	18
501 – 1,000	25
1,001 – 5,000	15
5,001 – 10,000	10
over 10,000	6
Number of Calgary employees (N = 316)	
Under 100	24
100 – 250	20
251 – 500	25
501 – 1,000	27
over 1,000	4

TABLE AP. I:2 Occupation and Organization Position of Respondents*

OCCUPATION	POSITION					PERCENTAGES
	Executive (12.19 per cent)	Managerial (22.4 per cent)	Supervisory (23.0 per cent)	Professional (39.4 per cent)	Technical (3.2 per cent)	
Manager-Administrator	6	27	1	0	0	9.8
Engineer	14	24	23	43	1	29.9
Geologist	10	15	24	51	3	29.6
Geophysicist	1	4	10	20	1	10.3
Accountant	5	5	15	13	1	11.2
Technologist	0	0	4	1	4	2.6
Other	6	3	4	9	1	6.6
						100

*N = 348

TABLE AP. I:3 Personal Demographic Sample Characteristics

CHARACTERISTIC	PERCENTAGE OF RESPONDENTS	CHARACTERISTIC	PERCENTAGE OF RESPONDENTS
Age (N = 347)		*Country Raised* (N = 349)	
23 – 29 years	12	Canada	79
30 – 45 years	45	U.S.A.	9
46 – 67 years	43	U.K.	5
		Europe	5
Sex (N = 350)		Other	3
Male	99	*Province/State Raised* (N = 304)	
Female	1	West	80
Marital Status (N = 349)		East	11
Single	2	U.S.	9
Married	95	*Citizenship* (N = 347)	
Other	3	Canadian	91
Yearly Income (N = 348)		U.S.	6
Under $15,000	9	Other	2
$15,000 – $19,999	24	*Political Preference*	
$20,000 – $29,000	46	*Provincial* (N = 316)	
$30,000 plus	21	Conservative	79
Education (N = 349)		SC	18
High school/Technical	7	Liberal	2
Bachelor's degree	60	NDP	1
Master's Degree/CA	15	*Federal* (N = 325)	
PHD	5	Conservative	76
Other	13	Liberal	21
		SC	2
		NDP	1

survey was used, then, to test and extend our information on certain tentative hypotheses, as well as to discover new information.[8] On the whole, although all of the scales used were clearly imperfect measuring devices, we are encouraged to accord them some general validity because of the high level of agreement between the survey findings and the findings from personal interviews. I will discuss each of the main scales briefly.

Job Satisfaction (Part II of questionnaire, first section)

The scale used was adapted from the Minnesota Satisfaction Questionnaire (short form), with modifications to make the questions suitable for professional workers in the oil industry. For example, question seven was changed to read "I often consider leaving the oil industry" rather than "...this company". The scale subsumes six sub-scales measuring various facets of job satisfaction: pay, recognition, co-workers, advancement, superiors, and commitment. We obtained a score for over-all satisfaction by summing the scores on each of the sub-scales. To check the validity of the scores, in a different part of the questionnaire we included the questions: "Over-all, how do you feel about: a. your present job? b. working for your present company? c. being employed in the oil industry?" The scores on these questions correlated quite highly with the scores on the over-all scale, with Pearson correlation coefficients of 0.59, 0.68, and 0.52 respectively.

Participation in Decision-Making (Part II questionnaire, second section)

This scale was partly adapted from Aiken and Hage (Price, 1972: 44 – 47), although we added a number of questions to cover areas of decision-making important to oilmen, and rephrased the question format to make it more concise.

Economic Conservatism (Part III of questionnaire, first section)

The scale we chose for economic conservatism was the subscale by that name from the long form of the Minnesota Survey of Opinions (Miller, 1970: 240 – 52). This scale caused some problems because many of the items were phrased ambiguously, and some respondents reacted to it with hostility. Unintentionally, however, this ambiguity proved useful in provoking responses that gave us better insights into the oilmen's breed of conservatism.

Alienation (Part IV of questionnaire)

The alienation scale was taken from Shepard (1973: 61 – 88), who devised measures of five types of alienation: powerlessness, meaninglessness, self-evaluative involvement, isolation from organizational goals, and instrumental work orientation. Since he conceived of each of these as being qualitatively different, Shepard refrained from computing scores for over-all alienation. But, as we were more interested in the general picture and did not want to belabour the discussion by detailed analyses of each of the sub-scales, we decided to sum the scores from each to arrive at an over-all score for alienation. Many of the items on these scales are ambiguous as well, and what is really being measured is sometimes unclear. It is worth noting that, on the most unambiguous sub-scale—powerlessness—oilmen showed up as least alienated.

Formalization (Part V of questionnaire, items 1 – 10)

We developed two measures of formalization adapted from Hage and Aiken, and Inkson, Pugh, and Hickson (Price, 1972: 107 – 17); these were job codification and imposition of structure. The former refers to the extent to which the activities pertaining to the job itself are formally prescribed, the latter to the extent to which behavioural expectations are continually being imposed by "the organization".

Achievement Opportunity (Part V of questionnaire, item 11)

This scale, based on four questions dealing with opportunities for achievement relating specifically to the job itself, proved to be our most important correlate with both job satisfaction and alienation. The items within the scale were adapted from Patchen (1970: 55 – 124).

Other Job-Related Characteristics (Part VI of questionnaire)

The items in this part of the questionnaire were all taken from Patchen (1965, 1970), and form the bases for the scales of job involvement and job participation. We sympathized with Patchen's attempt to develop more sophisticated measures of the context of people's work and the nature of their jobs, but found that some simplification was necessary in order to use the material collected for our variable analysis. While it is clear that the qualities of the work situation investigated by Patchen are important determinants of job satisfaction, we did not muster up the time and energy to develop the more detailed analysis that an exhaustive treatment of the data for this section might allow. Some of the questions were both difficult to answer (for the respondents) and difficult to code (for the investigators).

SECONDARY DATA SOURCES

Reliance upon primary data sources had two weaknesses for the study: it made it difficult to place the processes observed and discussed in a wider perspective, and it tended to produce an interpretation of the industry overly sympathetic to the oilmen themselves.[9] In an effort to balance this, I turned to secondary sources. There is an enormous body of literature on the international oil industry, and a growing one for Canada. Broadly, the literature falls into four main classes by source: industry publications, government reports, liberal-academic and journalistic accounts, and radical critiques. Each of these had its uses and limitations for our purposes. Industry periodicals and books contain a great deal of information about the industry, although this is presented in terms of (and has helped to mould) the same perspective as the oilmen we studied. Despite its heavy industry bias, I found *Oilweek* magazine an invaluable source of up-to-date information about the Canadian oil and gas picture. Government publications contain much of the same kind of information, but place it in the context of longer-term energy requirements and policy-making. In Canada, in particular, governments have relied upon the industry for their information and also, until recently at least, for their point of view. More critical perspectives are expressed in government publications from other countries: the Middle East, Norway, Great Britain, and even the United States where Congress seems to be involved in a perpetually unsuccessful anti-trust campaign against the oil companies.

Liberal-academic and journalistic accounts are useful for gaining a general overview of the international oil industry, although there is very little on Canadian aspects. These accounts tend to be more objective than other sources, and contain a lot of descriptive information. For the most part, however, they are lacking in a more comprehensive, theoretical interpretation and perspective. The radical literature, by contrast, provides the best counter-position to the oilmen's views, and is the best informed theoretically. This is both a strength and a weakness. On the one hand, it provides a powerful framework for interpreting both events within the industry and relations between the industry and governments in terms of a comprehensive theory of contemporary capitalist development. On the other hand, the heavy commitment to this view makes the interpretation of events one-sided and empirically shaky. Research is too much a matter of finding facts to fit the given theory rather than a genuine attempt to test the theory or to discover new information for grounding new theories.

All of these secondary data sources have been useful for the present study. Throughout the analysis, however, except in the concluding chapter, I have attempted to remain true to the primary data, and to present as objective an account as possible of the Calgary oil industry and community.[10]

DURATION OF THE STUDY

The study was conceived during the fall of 1972, while I was in the second year of an appointment as Assistant Professor of Sociology at the University of Calgary. I was interested in economic sociology, believed that social scientists should do work relevant to local issues, and had become sociologically curious about the oil industry. I had heard that Imperial Oil Limited provided no-strings-attached funding for various kinds of academic research and was interested in more projects in the social sciences. I applied for a grant to study the oil industry and its relationship to the community, with particular emphasis upon Imperial, and was surprised in the spring of 1973 to hear that they had agreed to fund the research for two years. The bulk of the interviewing and observation was done during the summers of 1973 and 1974. We did some interviewing during the autumn, winter, and spring of 1973 – 74, but most of that time was taken up with teaching and administrative duties at the university. The survey was conducted in the summer of 1974. The data analysis was begun in Calgary in the winter of 1974 – 75 and completed at Memorial University in Newfoundland, where I took up a new position in the fall of 1975. I spent over a year away from Calgary before returning briefly in the fall of 1976 to attend a faculty-company forum sponsored by Mobil Oil Canada Limited. If my period away from the oil community was useful for gaining distance and perspective, the brief but intensive return rekindled my enthusiasm for the project and conviction that my findings rang true. I began writing up the initial draft of this manuscript upon returning to Memorial, completed it in the summer of 1977, and added some revisions in the summer of 1978.

CONCLUSION

The proliferation of methodology textbooks and of undergraduate and graduate courses in research methods and statistics in recent years has obscured the fact that there are no clear-cut formulas for doing sociology. The discrepancy between neat formulations and an untidy empirical world is brought home when the attempt to conduct a research project is motivated by curiosity about some core institution of contemporary society, rather than by methodological predispositions. Certainly that has been our experience in attempting a sociological investigation of the oil industry in Calgary.

I suspect that too rigid an adherence to the positivist philosophy of science and its narrow assumptions about the relationship between theory and research is stultifying to the sociological imagination. Unwittingly, perhaps, it has led us to choose our problems to suit our methods and (perhaps) our need to produce easily publishable results. This problem might not be so bad if one could feel confident that the work being done is laying the groundwork for a better understanding of society in the future. That, too, is part of the positivist faith, but recent work in the philosophy, history, and sociology of science indicates that that faith may be misplaced. The natural sciences have enjoyed their tremendous progress in spite of, not because of, the positivist model.

I believe that the realist model of science, although not perfect, gives a better approximation of scientific practice, and deserves greater attention from sociologists. If science is conceived of as the description of natural systems and the search for the underlying causal mechanisms that give rise to the states, processes, and relations that constitute those systems, then sociology should be shifting its orientation.

One important implication of such a shift is rather mundane. It is that a great deal more research effort should go into the description of the various institutional systems that constitute modern societies. This need for empirical description is even greater in the social than the natural sciences because the systems themselves are continually changing. Such work is less glamorous than constructing new grand theories, providing learned interpretations of classical and modern theorists, or even testing known theories with sophisticated methodological techniques. But it has its own fascination, and is absolutely necessary if we are to gain in knowledge about our own society, which surely is the fundamental goal of the social sciences.

This book has described the oilmen of Calgary, their industry, and their community. The description is grounded in an investigation which used an untidy combination of methods in an open-ended, exploratory way. I am not suggesting that theories are or should be irrelevant. On the contrary, the study was conducted in terms of numerous theoretical preconceptions and concepts, many of them implicit. Nevertheless, I have tried to allow the data to speak for themselves as far as possible throughout most of the analysis. And in the final chapter I have attempted to draw out some of the more general, theoretical messages of the study for our understanding of the contemporary capitalist oil industry and its implications for Canadian society.

Finally, the study implies that any natural-science model—positivist, realist, phenomenological, or whatever—is insufficient by itself for guiding sociological research. Sociology is about human beings, and is therefore akin to the humanities in a way that the natural sciences are not. If this book makes possible some empathetic appreciation of the social and psychological world of the Calgary oilmen, then it has attained some measure of success.

Appendix II. Supplementary Tables

TABLE AP. II:1   Sex of Survey Sample of Calgary Oilmen

SEX	NUMBER	PER CENT
Male	347	99.1
Female	3	0.9
Total	350	100.0

TABLE AP. II:2   Marital Status of Survey Sample of Calgary Oilmen

MARITAL STATUS	NUMBER	PER CENT
Married	330	94.6
Single	7	2.0
Separated	5	1.4
Divorced	4	1.1
Widowed	3	0.9
Total	349	100.0

TABLE AP. II:3   Country of Origin of Survey Sample of Calgary Oilmen

COUNTRY	NUMBER	PER CENT	CUMULATIVE PER CENT
England and Wales	129	38.1	38.1
Scotland	47	13.9	51.9
Northern Ireland	34	10.0	61.9
France	12	3.5	65.5
Germany	39	11.5	77.0
Russia (Ukraine)	16	4.7	81.7
Poland	12	3.5	85.2
Other	50	14.8	100.0
Total	339	100.0	

TABLE AP. II:4   Number in Sample by Number of Their Company's
                 Employees in Canada

EMPLOYEES IN CANADA	NUMBER IN SAMPLE	PER CENT OF SAMPLE	CUMULATIVE PER CENT
1 – 99	59	18.2	18.2
100 – 499	66	20.4	38.6
500 – 999	85	26.2	64.8
1,000 – 4,999	58	17.9	82.7
5,000 – 9,999	31	9.6	92.3
10,000 – 15,999	25	7.7	100.0
Total	324		

TABLE AP. II:5   Organizational Level by Employee-Related Decision-
                 Making (Per Cent)

ORGANIZATIONAL LEVEL	PARTICIPATION IN DECISION-MAKING				
	Very Low	*Fairly Low*	*Fairly High*	*Very High*	*N*
Nonsupervisory/ Nonprofessional	81.5	9.1	9.1	-	11
Professional Workers	46.7	35.0	13.1	5.1	137
Supervisory	11.2	27.5	38.7	22.5	80
Jr. Managerial	5.1	10.3	34.6	50.0	78
Sr. Managerial	-	5.1	20.5	74.4	39
					345

Gamma = 0.75; Somer's D (Symmetric) = 0.57.

TABLE AP. II:6   Organizational Level by Organizationally Related
                 Decision-Making (Per Cent)

ORGANIZATIONAL LEVEL	PARTICIPATION IN DECISION-MAKING				
	Very Low	*Fairly Low*	*Fairly High*	*Very High*	*N*
Nonsupervisory/ Nonprofessional	54.5	27.3	18.2	-	11
Professional Workers	38.0	49.6	8.8	3.6	137
Supervisory	20.0	43.8	23.7	12.5	80
Jr. Managerial	14.1	17.9	28.2	39.7	78
Sr. Managerial	-	12.5	12.5	75.0	40
					346

Gamma = 0.63; Somer's D (Symmetric) = 0.49.

TABLE AP. II:7   Organizational Level by Job Codification
(Formalization) (Per Cent)

| ORGANIZATIONAL LEVEL | JOB CODIFICATION | | | | |
	Very Low	Fairly Low	Fairly High	Very High	N
Nonsupervisory/					
Nonprofessional	-	36.4	36.4	27.3	11
Professional Worker	19.7	38.7	27.0	14.6	137
Supervisory	17.5	33.7	26.2	22.5	80
Jr. Managerial	19.5	22.1	24.7	33.8	77
Sr. Managerial	41.5	41.5	9.8	7.3	41
					346

Gamma = −0.05; Somer's D (Symmetric) = −0.03.

TABLE AP. II:8   Organizational Level by Imposition of Structure
(Formalization) (Per Cent)

| ORGANIZATIONAL LEVEL | IMPOSITION OF STRUCTURE | | | | |
	Very Low	Fairly Low	Fairly High	Very High	N
Nonsupervisory/					
Nonprofessional	9.1	9.1	36.4	45.5	11
Professional Worker	16.8	29.2	29.2	24.3	137
Supervisory	18.7	37.5	23.7	20.0	80
Jr. Managerial	18.2	33.8	28.6	19.5	77
Sr. Managerial	41.5	29.3	17.1	12.2	41
					346

Gamma = −0.20; Somer's D (Symmetric) = −0.15.

TABLE AP. II:9   Organizational Level by Powerlessness (Per Cent)

| ORGANIZATIONAL LEVEL | POWERLESSNESS | | | | |
	Very Low	Fairly Low	Fairly High	Very High	N
Nonsupervisory/					
Nonprofessional	18.2	18.2	63.6	0	11
Professional Worker	30.7	37.2	26.3	5.8	137
Supervisory	35.0	41.2	18.7	5.0	80
Jr. Managerial	40.3	29.9	24.7	5.2	77
Sr. Managerial	75.6	22.2	0	2.4	41
					346

Gamma = −0.29; Somer's D (Symmetric) = −0.21.

TABLE AP. II:10 Regression Analysis, Variables Related to Job Satisfaction, Sample of Calgary Oilmen

VARIABLE	MULTIPLE R	R SQUARE	R SQ CHANGE	SIMPLE R	B	BETA
Achievement						
Opportunity	0.59808	0.35769	0.35769	0.59808	1.26702	0.46114
Job Involvement	0.62897	0.39561	0.03791	0.43352	1.22246	0.20384
Job						
Participation	0.64182	0.41193	0.01633	0.34520	0.31815	0.19759
Job Codification	0.65828	0.43334	0.02140	0.00608	0.41931	0.15858
(Constant)					11.35982	

TABLE AP. II:11 Regression Analysis, Variables Related to Subjective Alienation, Sample of Calgary Oilmen

VARIABLE	MULTIPLE R	R SQUARE	R SQ CHANGE	SIMPLE R	B	BETA
Achievement						
Opportunity	0.53601	0.28731	0.28731	−0.53601	−1.55123	−0.29578
Decision-Making	0.59926	0.35911	0.07180	−0.48594	−0.28548	−0.18194
Job Codification	0.64016	0.40981	0.05070	0.30979	1.19565	0.23690
Job Involvement	0.66576	0.44324	0.03343	−0.45311	−2.28576	−0.19967
Income	0.67175	0.45125	0.00801	0.37857	1.32206	0.10682
(Constant)					97.36807	

Appendix III. Sample Interview Schedule

Oil Companies in Calgary Interview Schedule

Date: _____

1. Name of Interviewer _____
2. Name of Company _____
3. Address of Calgary Office _____ Phone No. _____
4. Head Office Location of Company _____
5. Name of Interviewee _____
6. Position of Interviewee _____

SECTION A. ECONOMICS AND ORGANIZATION

7. Could you please tell me something about the ownership of this company? (Public corporation, subsidiary, majority shares owned by another company, etc.)

8. How does the company finance its local operations? (Budget from head office, reinvest profits, issue shares or bonds, bank loans, etc.)

9. What types of operations are the company involved in, and in what major locations?

	Involvement	*Locations*
a. Exploration		
b. Production		
c. Transportation		
d. Refining		
e. Marketing		
f. Research		
g. Other (Please specify)		

10. What types of operations are based in Calgary, and how important are these in overall company operations?

11. Could you tell me something about the history of the company, particularly concerning its operations in Calgary and Alberta?

12. Could you tell me (or give a reasonable estimate) of the number of employees the company has?
    a. Total   c. In Alberta
    b. In Canada   d. In Calgary

13. Approximately what proportion of those employed in Canada are Canadians? And at what levels?

14. Could you tell me something about the *organization* of the company's operations in Calgary? (Some sort of organizational chart would be very helpful).

15. Could you tell me something about the scale of operations of this company? (E.g. assets, profits. If we could have a copy of the company's *1972 Annual Report*, it would be very helpful.)

16. Do you know anything about how the company prices its products?

SECTION B. OIL AND THE COMMUNITY

17. What sorts of changes have you seen in the oil business in recent years, and what further directions of change do you foresee?

18. What sorts of changes have occurred in relations between the oil business and the government? Between the oil business and the public?

19. How do you feel about government regulation and involvement in the oil business in Calgary, Alberta, and Canada?

20. How do you view the future involvement of your company in Calgary and Alberta?

21. Does your company have any business interests locally other than in oil? (E.g. a. shares of other companies b. involvement in real estate investment and development.)

22. Is the company involved in any non-business interests in the community? (E.g. a. charities b. sponsor research.)

SECTION C. OCCUPATION AND CAREER

23. Could you tell me something about your own interest and involvement in the oil business?

24. How long have you been working in the oil business?

25. How long with this company?

26. What formal training have you had?

27. How do you like working in this business?
    a. main satisfactions.   b. main dissatisfactions.

28. What are your main aspirations?

29. What advice would you give a newcomer interested in working in the oil industry?

SECTION D. CONCLUDING QUESTIONS

30. Can you think of any other information that might interest us about your company, the oil business, and the relations of the oil industry to the local community?

31. Would it be possible for us to have a copy of the company's *1972 Annual Report*? Other company reports that might be of interest?

32. Do you know of any literature (books, periodicals, etc.) on the oil industry that might interest us?

33. This is an early, exploratory stage of our research. Do you feel that you and your company would be willing to co-operate further by:
    a. agreeing to another interview in, say, a year's time?
    b. supporting a mailed questionnaire survey of all (or a sample of) your employees?

Thank you very much for your time and co-operation in this project.

Appendix IV. Questionnaire

PART I

Following are a few general demographic questions concerning you and your position in the oil industry. These questions are to provide for group comparisons only and will *not* be used to identify individual respondents. Please check (√) the response category that applies to you, and where appropriate, write in a number or brief answer.

1. For how many years have you:
   a. Worked in the oil industry?
      [   ] yr(s)
   b. Been employed by your present company?
      [   ] yr(s)
   c. Been in your present position in the company?
      [   ] yr(s)

2. How many companies in the oil industry have you worked for?
   [   ]

3. How many positions have you held in your present company?
   [   ]

4. How are you paid by the company?
   ( ) Salary   ( ) Wages
   ( ) Other: _____

5. Do you participate in a profit-sharing, stock-option, or company-supported savings plan?
   ( ) Yes   ( ) No

6. Do you belong to any associations or clubs wherein you socialize with other members of the oil industry?
   ( ) Yes   ( ) No
         ↓
   Please specify: _____
   _____

7. What would you list as your occupation?
   _____

8. What is your present job title?
   _____

9. Please *briefly* explain the major duties associated with your job:
   _____
   _____

10. Within the company, approximately how many people report to you:
    a. Directly? [   ]
    b. Indirectly? [   ]

11. What is the approximate amount of organizational funds that you may commit without first securing senior approval?
    [$]

12. Your own work is primarily in the area of:
    ( ) Exploration
    ( ) Production
    ( ) Research and Development
    ( ) Land and Contracts
    ( ) Marketing
    ( ) Other: _____
    _____

13. Please indicate the extent of your formal education:
    ( ) C.A., C.G.A., R.I.A., or C.P.A.
    ( ) Master's Degree
    ( ) Some University (no degree)
    ( ) Bachelor's Degree
    ( ) High School
    ( ) Ph.D.
    ( ) Technical or Vocational Training. Specify: _____
    ( ) Other: _____

14. If you have a university degree, in which area(s) did you obtain your degree(s)?
    ( ) Geology ( ) Economics
    ( ) Business ( ) Chemistry
    ( ) Law   ( ) Geophysics
    ( ) Physics ( ) Engineering
    ( ) Other: _____

15. Please indicate the *type of company* by which you are employed:
    either by Name: _____
    or by answering the following 4 questions:
    a. Your company employs approximately how many persons:
       in Canada?
       in the Calgary area?
    b. The *primary* interest of your company is:
       ( ) Exploration
       ( ) Integrated
       ( ) Production
       ( ) Land
       ( ) Other: _____
    c. Is your company's head office located in:
       Calgary? ( ) Yes ( ) No
       Canada? ( ) Yes ( ) No
    d. Your company is best described as a(n):
       ( ) Major
       ( ) Independent
       ( ) Other: _____

PART II

We are interested in your opinions concerning your job so that we can compare the satisfactions associated with different types of jobs in and outside the oil industry. To the statements below, please indicate your degree of agreement or disagreement by checking (√) the appropriate response category:

SD = Strongly Disagree, D = Disagree, U = Undecided, A = Agree, SA = Strongly Agree

	SD	D	U	A	SA
1. The pay I receive is adequate for the job I do.	( )	( )	( )	( )	( )
2. I feel that my job enables me to do something really worthwhile.	( )	( )	( )	( )	( )
3. I am displeased with the company's promotion policy.	( )	( )	( )	( )	( )
4. I find there is a strong spirit of co-operation among my co-workers.	( )	( )	( )	( )	( )
5. I am dissatisfied with the competence of my supervisor in making decisions.	( )	( )	( )	( )	( )
6. I am pleased with the recognition I get for doing a good job.	( )	( )	( )	( )	( )
7. I often consider leaving the oil industry.	( )	( )	( )	( )	( )
8. For a person with my education, the oil industry offers good opportunities to get ahead.	( )	( )	( )	( )	( )
9. I get a strong feeling of accomplishment from my job.	( )	( )	( )	( )	( )
10. A person in my position should get a higher income than I receive.	( )	( )	( )	( )	( )
11. I find that my co-workers are quite unfriendly.	( )	( )	( )	( )	( )

12. I generally get along well with
    my supervisor.   ( ) ( ) ( ) ( ) ( )
13. The chances for advancement
    are very good on my job.   ( ) ( ) ( ) ( ) ( )
14. I often consider leaving my
    present company.   ( ) ( ) ( ) ( ) ( )
15. There are a number of good
    fringe benefits with my job.   ( ) ( ) ( ) ( ) ( )

With regard to *your present work environment:*

16. How frequently do you
    usually participate in the
    decision-making process
    regarding:

	Almost Never	Seldom	Some-times	Often	Almost Always
1. the need for new staff and qualifications required?	( )	( )	( )	( )	( )
2. the selection of new staff?	( )	( )	( )	( )	( )
3. the promotion of any of the professional staff?	( )	( )	( )	( )	( )
4. the adoption of new policies?	( )	( )	( )	( )	( )
5. the adoption of new programs?	( )	( )	( )	( )	( )
6. procedures involved in doing your job or assignment?	( )	( )	( )	( )	( )
7. ways in which integration between departments could be improved?	( )	( )	( )	( )	( )
8. ways in which satisfaction or morale among personnel could be improved?	( )	( )	( )	( )	( )

PART III

Listed below are a number of generalized statements often heard regarding various aspects of economic, political, and social life. We would appreciate your comment on such general statements. In each case, please check (✓) the response that most characterizes the degree to which you agree or disagree with each statement:

SD = Strongly Disagree, D = Disagree, U = Undecided, A = Agree, SA = Strongly Agree

	SD	D	U	A	SA
1. The government should take over all large industries.	( )	( )	( )	( )	( )
2. Labour should obey only those laws that seem reasonable.	( )	( )	( )	( )	( )
3. Legislatures are too ready to pass laws to curb business freedom.	( )	( )	( )	( )	( )
4. For men to do their best there must be the possibility of large profit.	( )	( )	( )	( )	( )
5. Poverty is chiefly a result of injustice in the distribution of wealth.	( )	( )	( )	( )	( )
6. Large incomes should be taxed much more than they are now.	( )	( )	( )	( )	( )
7. The more a man learns about an economic system, the less willing he is to see change made.	( )	( )	( )	( )	( )
8. The government should provide a guaranteed annual income.	( )	( )	( )	( )	( )
9. Men would not do their best if government owned all industry.	( )	( )	( )	( )	( )
10. Private ownership of property is necessary for economic progress.	( )	( )	( )	( )	( )

11. Our economic system is
    criticized too much.   ( ) ( ) ( ) ( ) ( )
12. Without sweeping changes in
    our economic system, little
    progress can be made in the
    solution of social problems.   ( ) ( ) ( ) ( ) ( )
13. The incomes of most people
    are a fair measure of their
    contribution to human
    welfare.   ( ) ( ) ( ) ( ) ( )
14. When a rich man dies, most
    of his property should go to
    the state.   ( ) ( ) ( ) ( ) ( )
15. On the whole our economic
    system is just and wise.   ( ) ( ) ( ) ( ) ( )
16. Labour does not get its fair
    share of what it produces.   ( ) ( ) ( ) ( ) ( )
17. A man should strike in order
    to secure greater returns to
    labour.   ( ) ( ) ( ) ( ) ( )

The following questions deal with the relationship between the oil
industry and various government bodies.

	Very Poor	Poor	Fair	Good	Very Good
1. How would you rate the performance of the Alberta Energy Resources Conservation Board in regulating the oil industry?	( )	( )	( )	( )	( )
2. How would you rate the current Alberta government in terms of its policies regarding the oil industry?	( )	( )	( )	( )	( )
3. How would you rate the current federal government in terms of its policies regarding the oil industry?	( )	( )	( )	( )	( )

PART IV

The series of questions and statements presented below have to do with your feelings about a number of characteristics associated with your job, the oil industry, and work in general. For each item you are asked to give a rating on a one-to-six (1 – 6) point scale that appears immediately below the item. Please *circle the number* on the scale that best represents *your particular feelings* in each case.

1. To what extent can you vary the steps involved in doing your job?
   (definitely not enough)   1 2 3 4 5 6   (sufficiently)

2. To what extent do you know how your job fits into the total work organization?
   (definitely not enough)   1 2 3 4 5 6   (sufficiently)

3. Your job is something you have to do to earn a living; most of your real interests are centred outside your job.
   (strongly disagree)   1 2 3 4 5 6   (strongly agree)

4. You would like people to judge you for the most part by what you spend your money on rather than by how you make your money.
   (strongly disagree)   1 2 3 4 5 6   (strongly agree)

5. To what extent can you move from your immediate working area during working hours?
   (definitely not enough)   1 2 3 4 5 6   (sufficiently)

6. To what extent do you know how your work contributes to company products?
   (definitely not enough)   1 2 3 4 5 6   (sufficiently)

7. To what extent can you control how much work you produce?
   (definitely not enough)   1 2 3 4 5 6   (sufficiently)

8. Money is the most rewarding reason for working.
   (strongly disagree)   1 2 3 4 5 6   (strongly agree)

9. Success in the things you do away from the job is more important to your opinion of yourself than success in your work career.
   (strongly disagree)   1 2 3 4 5 6   (strongly agree)

10. The reputation of the oil industry in the community is very important to you.
    (strongly disagree)   1 2 3 4 5 6   (strongly agree)

11. To what extent can you help decide on methods and procedures used in your job?
    (definitely not enough)   1 2 3 4 5 6   (sufficiently)

12. To what extent do you have influence over the things that happen to you at work?
(definitely not enough)   1 2 3 4 5 6   (sufficiently)

13. To you, work is only a small part of why you are.
(strongly disagree)   1 2 3 4 5 6   (strongly agree)

14. The only reason the industry's profits are important to you is that they affect the amount of money you make.
(strongly disagree)   1 2 3 4 5 6   (strongly agree)

15. To what extent do you know how your job fits into the work of other departments?
(definitely not enough)   1 2 3 4 5 6   (sufficiently)

16. To what extent can you increase or decrease the speed at which you work?
(definitely not enough)   1 2 3 4 5 6   (sufficiently)

17. To what extent do you know how your work affects the jobs of others you work with?
(definitely not enough)   1 2 3 4 5 6   (sufficiently)

18. Working is a necessary evil to provide things you and your family want.
(strongly disagree)   1 2 3 4 5 6   (strongly agree)

19. If you had to choose, you would much prefer that others judge you by the kind of job you hold, rather than by your off-the-job accomplishments.
(strongly disagree)   1 2 3 4 5 6   (strongly agree)

20. Cutting costs within the industry is of little importance to you.
(strongly disagree)   1 2 3 4 5 6   (strongly agree)

21. To what extent do you know how your job fits in with other jobs in the company?
(definitely not enough)   1 2 3 4 5 6   (sufficiently)

22. To what extent are you learning a great deal about the company while doing your job?
(definitely not enough)   1 2 3 4 5 6   (sufficiently)

23. To what extent can you do your work ahead and take a short rest break during work hours?
(definitely not enough)   1 2 3 4 5 6   (sufficiently)

24. You are living for the day when you can collect your retirement and do the things that are important to you.
(strongly disagree)   1 2 3 4 5 6   (strongly agree)

25. The best description of who you are would be based on the kind of job you hold.
(strongly disagree)   1 2 3 4 5 6   (strongly agree)

26. The quality of the industry's products is of little importance to you.
    (strongly disagree)   1 2 3 4 5 6   (strongly agree)

27. Further development and growth of the oil industry is very important to you.
    (strongly disagree)   1 2 3 4 5 6   (strongly agree)

28. To what extent are you free from close supervision while doing your job?
    (definitely not enough)   1 2 3 4 5 6   (sufficiently)

29. To what extent does management give you enough information about what is going on that affects your department?
    (definitely not enough)   1 2 3 4 5 6   (sufficiently)

PART V

Each of the following statements may or may not be true for your immediate situation in the oil industry. Again, for each item below, please answer by checking (√) that category which you feel best describes *your work environment*.

	Defi- nitely false	More false than true	More true than false	Defi- nitely true
1. Whatever situation arises, we have procedures to follow in dealing with it.	( )	( )	( )	( )
2. I have a specific job to do.	( )	( )	( )	( )
3. Going through the proper channels is constantly stressed.	( )	( )	( )	( )
4. How things are done in my job is left pretty much up to myself.	( )	( )	( )	( )
5. The organization keeps a detailed written record of my job performance.	( )	( )	( )	( )
6. I am to follow strict operating procedures at all times.	( )	( )	( )	( )
7. Whenever I have a problem, I am supposed to go to the same person for an answer.	( )	( )	( )	( )
8. Work norms here are quite explicit.	( )	( )	( )	( )
9. There is a complete written job description for my job.	( )	( )	( )	( )
10. Generally, I make up my own rules regarding my job.	( )	( )	( )	( )

11. In connection with your job, how much chance do you get:	Very little or no chance	Little chance	Some chance	A good chance	An exc- ellent chance
a. to do the kind of things you're best at?	( )	( )	( )	( )	( )
b. to show your full potential?	( )	( )	( )	( )	( )
c. to learn new things?	( )	( )	( )	( )	( )
d. to see your projects or assignments fully completed?	( )	( )	( )	( )	( )

12. Overall, how do you feel about:	Very dissat- isfied	Dissat- isfied	Indif- ferent	Satis- fied	Very satis- fied
a. your present job?	( )	( )	( )	( )	( )
b. working for your present company?	( )	( )	( )	( )	( )
c. being employed in the oil industry?	( )	( )	( )	( )	( )

PART VI

This group of questions and statements deals with participation and involvement in the job and is meant to gain a better understanding of a number of important job characteristics.

1. On most days on your job, how often does the time seem to drag for you?
   ( ) about 1/2 of the time or more
   ( ) about 1/3 of the day
   ( ) about 1/4 of the day
   ( ) about 1/8 of the day
   ( ) time never seems to drag

2. Some people are completely involved in their job—they are absorbed in it night and day. For other people, their job is simply one of several interests. How involved do you feel in your job?
   ( ) very little involved; my other interests are more absorbing
   ( ) slightly involved
   ( ) moderately involved; my job and my other interests are equally absorbing
   ( ) strongly involved
   ( ) very strongly involved; my work is the most absorbing interest in my life

3. In your kind of work, if a person tries to change his usual way of doing things, how does it generally turn out?
   ( ) usually turns out worse; the tried and true methods work best in my work
   ( ) usually doesn't make much difference
   ( ) usually turns out better; our methods need improvement

4. When you get a job to do, how often is it completely up to you to decide how to go about doing it?
   ( ) about 10% of the time or less
   ( ) about 25% of the time
   ( ) about 50% of the time
   ( ) about 75% of the time
   ( ) almost always

5. In some jobs, there are detailed rules about what is the right way to do the job. In other jobs a person can choose between several possible ways of doing the job. How is it with your job?
   ( ) almost everything is covered by rules
   ( ) most things are covered by rules
   ( ) about half and half
   ( ) on most things I have a choice of ways of doing the work
   ( ) on almost everything I have a choice of ways of doing the work

6. If you suggest to your immediate supervisor a way of doing some job, how often does he go along with your suggestions?
   ( ) about 10% of the time or less
   ( ) about 25% of the time
   ( ) about 50% of the time
   ( ) about 75% of the time
   ( ) almost always
   ( ) I never suggest a way of doing some job

7. How many times in the past year have you suggested to your supervisor a different or better way of doing something on the job?
   - ( ) never had occasion to do this during the past year
   - ( ) once or twice
   - ( ) about three times
   - ( ) about five times
   - ( ) six to seven times
   - ( ) more than ten times

8. In judging the quality of your work, how much is the person who checks your work influenced by what you tell him about the special problems or conditions you met in doing the job?
   - ( ) a great deal
   - ( ) quite a bit
   - ( ) somewhat
   - ( ) little
   - ( ) not at all

9. Before your supervisor sets deadlines, time limits, or target dates which involve your work, how often does he ask your opinion (either alone or as a member of a group) concerning how long the job will take?
   - ( ) 90% of the time or more
   - ( ) about 75% of the time
   - ( ) about 50% of the time
   - ( ) about 25% of the time
   - ( ) about 10% of the time or less

10. If someone asked you to describe yourself and you could tell only three things from the following list, in which order would you be most likely to answer? (Put a number *1* next to your first choice, a *2* next to your second choice, and a *3* next to your third)

____ I come from (your home province or state)
____ I work for (your company name)
____ I am a (your occupation or type of work)
____ I am a (your church preference)
____ I am a graduate of (your school name)
____ I am in the petroleum industry

11. In my kind of job, it's usually better to let your supervisor worry about new or better ways of doing things.
    - ( ) strongly agree
    - ( ) mostly agree
    - ( ) mostly disagree
    - ( ) strongly disagree

12. When you have several things to do on the job, how often is it up to you to decide which you will do first, and how often are you expected to do things in a set order?
    - ( ) almost always expected to do things in a set order
    - ( ) usually expected to follow a set order
    - ( ) usually up to me to decide which I'll do first
    - ( ) almost always up to me to decide

13. When your work has been looked over by a supervisor, how much say or influence do you have in deciding whether it should be changed or done over?
    - ( ) no say at all
    - ( ) little say
    - ( ) some say
    - ( ) quite a bit of say
    - ( ) a great deal of say

14. How much say or influence do you have (either alone or together with other people at about your level) when it comes to setting the time schedules for jobs that you work on?
    ( ) no influence at all
    ( ) little influence
    ( ) some influence
    ( ) quite a bit of influence
    ( ) a great deal of influence

15. When schedules or time limits are being set for work you are doing, in which order of importance do the following influence how these limits are set? (Put a number *1* next to the most important influence, a number *2* next to the second, and a number *3* next to the third)

____ Requirements of people outside your own section
____ Your own estimate of how long the job will take (or the estimate of yourself and other people at your level)
____ Your supervisor's estimate of how long it will take

16. How often do you get chances to try out your ideas on your job, either before or after checking with your supervisor?
    ( ) several times a week or more
    ( ) about once a week
    ( ) several times a month
    ( ) about once a month
    ( ) less than once a month

PART VII

This section looks at some of the characteristics which often serve to differentiate groups of people. Other research has shown that different backgrounds and life situations are often related to feelings about work. We would like to see if this also applies to people associated with the oil industry. Please check (√) the response category that applies to you and, where appropriate, write in a *brief* answer. Remember, *your answers are anonymous and confidential* and will only be reported in group statistics.

1. What is (or was) your father's regular occupation? _____
   If you feel it would provide a better explanation, please outline briefly the major duties associated with his job:
   _____
   _____

2. Please indicate your income range:
   ( ) 60,000 or more
   ( ) 50,000-59,999
   ( ) 40,000-49,999
   ( ) 30,000-39,999
   ( ) 20,000-29,999
   ( ) 15,000-19,999
   ( ) 12,500-14,999
   ( ) 10,000-12,499
   ( ) 7,500-9,999
   ( ) 5,000-7,499
   ( ) less than 5,000

3. Does a large share of your income come from investments (say 20% or more)?
   ( ) Yes   ( ) No

4. What is your religious preference (if any)?
   ( ) no preference
   ( ) Roman Catholic
   ( ) United Church
   ( ) Anglican
   ( ) Jewish
   ( ) Other ____

5. Your present age: [   ]

6. Your marital status:
   ( ) married
   ( ) single
   ( ) separated
   ( ) divorced
   ( ) widowed

7. Your sex:
   ( ) Female   ( ) Male

8. In which country were you raised?
   ( ) Canada
   ( ) United States
   ( ) Other: please specify
   _____

9. In which province, territory, or state were you raised?
   _____

10. Your present country of citizenship is:
    _____

11. Historically, from which country of the "old world" did your family originate?
    _____

Which generation of your
family first moved to North
America?
- ( ) my generation
- ( ) my parents' generation
- ( ) my grandparents'
  generation
- ( ) my great-grandparents'
  generation
- ( ) before my great-
  grandparents

12. Would you please give an
    indication of your political
    preference:

    A. Federally
    - ( ) Social Credit
    - ( ) Conservative
    - ( ) Liberal
    - ( ) NDP
    - ( ) Other ____

    B. Provincially
    - ( ) Social Credit
    - ( ) Conservative
    - ( ) Liberal
    - ( ) NDP
    - ( ) Other ____

PART VIII

Should you have any further comments or opinions concerning such things as your work, the petroleum industry, government involvement, foreign control, etc., we welcome them in the following space. (Please feel free to use the back cover if you wish.)

Thank you very much for your assistance in this study. We sincerely hope that you have found the questionnaire interesting.

Notes

CHAPTER ONE

1. These figures and those on the social organization of the industry are taken from the 1973 – 74 *Canadian Oil Register*. The number of companies varies from year to year. For a discussion of the uses and limitations of that source, see Appendix I.
2. The issues of foreign ownership and metropolis-hinterland relations are discussed in Chapter Two.
3. These data have been abstracted from the 1971 Census of Canada and may overstate the oil population somewhat by including a small number of geologists who do not work in the oil industry. There is a greater proportion of professional workers in Calgary than in Edmonton, and a greater proportion of the industry's manual workers in Edmonton than in Calgary.
4. The tool pusher makes decisions about when to use various types of equipment (e.g., when an additional length of piping should be added) and supervises the work of the drilling crew.
5. This organization is discussed in chapters Two and Three.
6. These data and those that follow (on the social composition of Calgary oilmen) are based on a survey conducted for this project in 1974. For a discussion of the survey, see Appendix I.
7. Various points throughout the text will be illustrated by direct quotations from personal interviews with Calgary oilmen. For a discussion of these interviews, see Appendix I.
8. See Appendix II, Table Ap. II:1.
9. For a complete breakdown by marital status, see Appendix II, Table Ap. II:2.
10. Political allegiances and religious beliefs are discussed in Chapter Six.
11. For a detailed breakdown by country of origin, see Appendix II, Table Ap. II:3.

CHAPTER TWO

1. This is discussed further in Chapter Four, and in J. D. House, "The Social Organization of Multinational Corporations: Canadian Subsidiaries in the Oil Industry", *Canadian Review of Sociology and Anthropology*, 1977, 14:1 – 14.
2. The information on Canadian companies is consolidated from *Canadian Business*'s "The Top 200", from *The Financial Post Survey of Oils, 1976*, and from our own interviews.
3. Source: Independent Petroleum Association of Canada.
4. About 15 per cent of the rights to oil and gas and minerals in Alberta are held freehold, that is as private property. The rest is held by the Crown. This is an important difference between the Canadian and the American oil scenes. In the United States, most oil and gas rights are freehold. This increases both the degree of anarchy in the industry and the proportion of people who get rich from oil and gas exploration.
5. Source: Independent Petroleum Association of Canada.

CHAPTER THREE

1. Such an approach has been common among structural sociologists since the pioneering works of Karl Marx and Max Weber. I will beg the important philosophical question about whether the logic is really "out there" in the social world or is simply imposed by the analyst to make sense of the data.
2. George Homans's claim for "ultimate psychological reductionism" is not so much wrong as it is trivial. Sociologists are interested in the proximate, not the ultimate, causes of behaviour; and many of these are structural (Homans, 1974).
3. Again, the initial insight was Marx's. He saw, on the one hand, that in their productive relations men are constrained by forces "independent of their will"; and on the other, that "men make their own history". I am using "dialectic" in a more general sense than orthodox Marxists do to refer to all relations among people and the social systems in which they participate.
4. A further breakdown of company size by number of employees for the sample is given in Appendix II, Table Ap. II:4.
5. In particular, it has been easy to acquire exploration rights. Early colonial land grants (which included mineral rights), for example, have allowed Canadian Pacific and the Hudson's Bay Company,

as well as some smaller land-grant companies (such as Canada Northwest Land Limited), to establish themselves firmly in the oil business.

6. For convenience, I will use the term "service company" here to include drilling, service-and-supply, and consultant companies. They all provide services of one kind or another to the oil companies.

7. These deals are discussed later in this chapter.

8. The majors are not always successful in this and sometimes, particularly in frontier areas, find themselves paying very high prices for specialist services.

9. The use of service companies also promotes flexibility within the industry, which benefits the majors.

10. The Organization of Petroleum Export Countries represents the interests of the major oil and gas exporting countries. It has engineered the dramatic increases in the world price of crude oil since 1973.

11. The concerns for security, smooth operations, and predictability are also important "motives" for most companies.

12. Canadian oilmen are not knowledgeable about the Soviet Union. "Russian inefficiency" is best viewed as part of their faith. A Soviet colleague of mine dismisses such arguments and insists instead that the Soviet system with its rational, planned, systematic approach is much more efficient. I will return to these issues in the concluding chapter.

13. There may be some backroom deals involved, but an assumption of such overt collusion is not necessary to understand the logic of the agreements.

14. I was told that American anti-trust authorities would never approve of such an arrangement. Canadian authorities, *and* Canadian oilmen, are less "free enterprise" in this respect.

15. A "gusher" is a commercial oil or gas producer.

16. According to a study that focused upon oil-company location, 90 per cent of all oil companies in Calgary had their offices in the central area in 1969–70 (Zieber, 1971: 162).

17. The well is said to be "spudded" when the drilling company has started drilling the hole.

18. Apparently, this sort of thing does happen in at least some other types of business, for example bond trading. The point is, however, that oilmen *perceive* this informality as special to their own community.

19. Flexibility and adaptability characterize the international oil scene as well, as witness the industry's success in rationing petroleum to consuming countries during the 1973 – 74 oil crisis, and in adapting to new types of profitable business operations after the Arab takeover of its Middle East production.

20. Oilmen conveniently ignore the *costs* of the system caused by outflows of surplus capital, land hoarding, duplication of efforts, and wasteful exploratory drilling. The system as a whole is assessed more fully in the concluding chapter.

CHAPTER FOUR

1. The reader is reminded that I am restricting my analysis to professional, managerial, and entrepreneurial oilmen. The mechanical model probably approximates better to the work of many secretaries and non-professional workers.

2. Although I will be depicting an ideal/typical model of a major oil company, the main source of data is Imperial Oil Limited's Calgary-based operations.

3. In using the term "genius" here, I do not mean to eulogize capitalist business corporations. Indeed, I have serious doubts about the extent to which this genius is being employed in the public interest.

4. For a more extended treatment of the topic of this section and its implications for the Canadianization of the oil industry, see J. D. House, "The Social Organization of Multinational Corporations: Canadian Subsidiaries in the Oil Industry", *Canadian Review of Sociology and Anthropology*, 1977, 14:1 – 14.

5. For a more detailed and technical presentation of these data, see Appendix II, Tables Ap. II:5 – Ap. II:9.

6. Not all professional employees agree. Some, particularly those involved in more routine technical work, feel alienated and isolated from decision-making. I will discuss this further in Chapter Five.

7. This is *not* to suggest that there are no individual differences. Contrary to some radical stereotypes, mere conformists do not make it to the top. Some evidence of originality and innovativeness in leadership is necessary for career success at this level.

8. No one was able (willing?) to tell me how many people were laid off, nor where the decision to lay them off originated. Senior Imperial managers claimed that it was an Imperial decision. Others were suspicious of this claim because, they maintained,

similar lay-offs occurred at Exxon's American subsidiary, Humble Oil, at the same time. These facts are less important for the present purpose than details of the effects upon the people involved and upon the organization.

9. This account is based upon an interview with the person involved, and has been corroborated by three other company employees. I have used a pseudonym, and have altered some of the non-essential details to protect the identity of the individual.

CHAPTER FIVE

1. As against certain contemporary trends in the sociology of knowledge, this social structural reality is viewed here as real in its own terms, not simply as a nominal construction. This realist view is consistent with the early formulation of the problem by Karl Marx (Keat and Urry, 1975). I am not using "dialectical" in the Marxist sense. (See note 3 to Chapter Three.)

2. The reader is reminded that I am constructing an ideal/typical career pattern here. There are many individual variations.

3. This purely technical background may help explain why Canadian oilmen seem to experience difficulty, by their own admission, in dealing with governments and the public.

4. By contrast, many oilmen in Britain today view their involvement in the industry as a step towards leaving the country with its (in their view) high levels of taxation and its economic problems.

5. Note that this is an analytical distinction. Entrepreneurial expansion of the organization as a whole is also a means to career advancement in large companies; and, to the extent that they do progress up the few organizational levels available, there is an element of organizational careerism for oilmen in small companies.

6. This is not to suggest that all deal-makers are older oilmen. Some move into this from the majors while fairly young, some move from small oil companies, and some deal-makers are non-professionals.

CHAPTER SIX

1. For an extended treatment of this theme, see Appendix I.

2. Wayne Rowe of the Regional College of Memorial University at

Corner Brook carried out most of the statistical analysis for this chapter, and is the co-author of this section.

3. By "alienation" here, we mean subjective alienation, the extent to which oilmen *feel* themselves to be involved with or psychologically disassociated from the work they do. In an objective, Marxist sense, oilmen are by definition alienated as workers within a capitalist system (see Horton, 1964). Such a designation, we feel, is too inclusive as it begs the important question of why at least some groups of workers feel satisfied and non-alienated within the contemporary capitalist work world. This chapter attempts an explanation of this for one group of such privileged workers, Calgary oilmen.

4. The use of regression analysis may be questioned here, as the data do not meet the requirements for an interval scale. We feel justified in using the technique, however, both for economy of expressing the findings and because analysis using other techniques which do not require the same strict assumptions about the data (such as multiple-classification analysis) turned up consistently similar findings.

5. Again, the reader should be reminded of the limits to the scope of this analysis. We are not suggesting that all groups working in the oil industry are satisfied.

6. For ease of expression, we will use "job satisfaction" as a general term to subsume low subjective alienation as well, except where otherwise specified. The two are closely related ($r = -0.47$ for the over-all scales), and it is far from clear that they are distinct measures of distinctly separate variables.

7. The following account is by one of only two female engineers that I interviewed. I am not sure about how her sex related to her unhappiness; but it seems likely that it acted as a career mobility barrier that kept her in the less interesting jobs. The other female engineer, who worked for a different major, was both more successful and more satisfied.

8. This empirical generalization could, unfortunately, be given an anti-democratic authoritarian bent. But there is no necessary connection between the two, and a social scientist's democratic values should not blind him or her to what is empirically the case.

9. It appears that disguised values (democracy, the protestant ethic with regard to work) are built into the supposedly objective measures of alienation.

10. These comments should not be taken to demean the use of "alienation" as a purely philosophical term in an avowedly subjectivist and evaluative sense. This is the way in which it was used by Hegel, Feuerbach, and the young Marx (Hook, 1962). Perhaps the realization of this limitation explains why Marx stopped using the term in his later work which focused more upon the *science* than the philosophy of man.

CHAPTER SEVEN

1. For my own interpretation of these events, see Chapter Eight.
2. Of 350 completed questionnaires, 149 respondents added general comments. Of these, 114 dealt with political and economic beliefs and commentary.
3. The oilmen's arguments seem particularly weak on this issue, and are obviously biased by narrow economic self-interest. It is a peculiar argument to claim that we should let our petroleum supplies run out so that we can find new reserves so that our supplies will not run out. And surely no responsible government can accept the industry's blind faith in the timely development of alternative sources of energy. On this issue, it seems clear that Canadian oil is too important to leave to Canadian oilmen.
4. For a discussion of American tax policy and petroleum drilling funds, see above, pp. 17-18.
5. This chronicle of events on the international oil scene is taken from a special issue of *Daedalus* (1975: 283 – 84).
6. This summary is taken from *An Energy Strategy For Canada* (1976: 156 – 58).

CHAPTER EIGHT

1. For a discussion of the way in which the research methods may have biased the conclusions, see Appendix I, p. 172.
2. This approach accords with my interpretation of what Karl Mannheim was attempting in his perspectivist method (Mannheim, 1936; House, 1977c). No claim is being made here for objectivity in any absolute sense. I am presenting a personal view which may be of interest to others.
3. In the inimitable Canadian political tradition, the liberal critics have been mainly members of the Progressive Conservative party, favouring small business and nationalist economic policies.

4. In other words, I will be constructing an ideal type of the critics' point of view based upon the literature already cited, which may not coincide exactly with any particular critic's position.

5. An important qualifier is in order here. Had the oil and gas been produced and transported by extended pipelines to eastern Canada, the current short-term supply prospects might have been equally precarious, possibly at greater economic cost during that period of cheap foreign oil.

6. Oligopolistic control rests upon a mutual recognition of self-interests in avoiding price competition, rather than upon overt collusion. See the discussion above, pp. 45-46.

7. For a given ratio of productive labour to population, the material standard of living of a nation depends ultimately upon the productivity of labour, which in turn depends upon the level of technology and the efficiency with which work is organized.

8. This assumes that a high material standard of living is accepted as a positive social value. Given the proviso that this value is achieved neither at the expense of other values, such as protecting the natural environment, nor through exploiting people in other countries, I think most people (including both oilmen and their critics) would agree with it.

9. The Western economist assumes that a free-market system ensures the most rational organization of production and distribution of goods and services by balancing supply with effective demand. But this is "rational" only if one assumes a market determination of returns to labour and capital, a system that is itself the major source of social inequality in a market society. Hence, effective demand may have little to do with individual and social need, that is with substantive rationality under a different set of social values, as in the Soviet Union.

10. There are, however, conflicts among the three ministries involved: geology, oil, and gas.

11. The analysis in this section is based upon information from a number of sources which I cannot distinguish individually. The list of References at the end includes these sources.

12. These countries have been excluded from the analysis above. They were not major actors in the series of events, merely its major victims.

13. "A blunt instrument" because higher prices, by themselves, do not necessarily lead to higher rates of exploration. Indeed, frontier exploration has been *declining* in Canada while prices have been rising.

14. In this regard, it is worth noting the existence of a secret committee, the National Advisory Committee on Petroleum, which comprises senior oil executives, and meets every two months in Ottawa with various ministers and top officials. The members are sworn to secrecy and, according to the President of Mobil Oil, the committee has greater influence upon energy policy than either the IPAC, the CPA, or any other form of industry lobbying.

15. According to Imperial Oil, for an $8 barrel of standard crude in Alberta, $3.12 goes in royalties to Alberta, $2.51 in income tax to the federal government, and $1.69 to the company. According to the PPAC, when tax incentives and depletion allowances are taken into account, the company receives $3.41 and only 79¢ goes in income taxes. (It seems to me that the latter proportions must understate the federal government's share).

16. I have specified American-owned because by far the greatest share of foreign ownership is American.

17. With the notable exception of the Berger report. But the federal government's rapid adoption of the alternative Alcan route for the gas pipeline from Alaska to the lower forty-eight states suggests that the rejection of the Mackenzie Valley proposal does *not* represent an important policy change.

APPENDIX I

1. This is not a call for a return to empiricism (which is a view of science as research completely divorced from theorizing) but a call for the disciplining of new sociological theorizing by continued empirical research.

2. By "narrow sense" I mean problems about what research techniques to use and how to use them. The preceding discussion has been about methodology in a broader, more philosophical sense.

3. The exclusive reliance upon secondary sources of data tends to make much critical social science stilted and dehumanized. Concerned with the weaknesses of capitalism as a system, critics tend to forget that businessmen are people, too.

4. Critics may suspect the company's motives in this reluctance; but it may be sobering for academics and others to consider how they would feel about having a sociologist attend and take notes on their department meetings.

5. The oil companies' refusal to provide this kind of information is, however, a serious impediment to developing a knowledgeable *political economy* of the industry.

6. The way in which the meetings were run impressed me favoura- bly compared to the format of meetings in the only other organi- zations in which I have attended department meetings — universi- ties and a real estate company (House, 1977b).

7. I would like to thank Larry Deboice for letting me use Tables Ap. I: 1, I:2, and I:3, which he prepared for his MA thesis (Deboice, 1975).

8. We had the impression from the Imperial interviews, for example, that a large proportion of Calgary oilmen were British. The more systematic survey data showed that this was not the case. The first impression reflects Imperial's practice during the sixties of hiring in Britain, a practice that was apparently not followed by most other companies.

9. This is to some degree an example of the temptation, familiar to social anthropologists, to "go native". But more than this, al- though I was never tempted to turn oilman, I think the primary data methods themselves have a built-in bias favourable to the people investigated.

10. Although I agree with those who maintain that complete objectiv- ity is impossible in social science, I see that insight as dangerous if it is used as a licence to avoid doing sound empirical research. Although absolute truth is an impossible goal, we must aim for as nearly correct a conceptual representation of empirical social sys- tems as possible (House, 1977c).

References

Baran, Paul A. and Paul M. Sweezy.
1966 *Monopoly Capital.* New York: Modern Reader.

Barth, Fredrik, ed.
1963 *The Social Role of the Entrepreneur in Social Change in Northern Norway.* Bergen: Universitetsforlaget.

Belshaw, Cyril.
1955 "The Cultural Milieu of the Entrepreneur: A Critical Essay". *Explorations in Entrepreneurial History,* 7: 146 – 63.

Berger, Peter L.
1963 *Invitation to Sociology: A Humanistic Perspective.* Garden City, New York: Doubleday Anchor.

Berger, Thomas R.
1977 *Northern Frontier, Northern Homeland: The Report of the Mackenzie Valley Pipeline Inquiry: Volume One.* Ottawa: Supply and Services Canada.

Berle, Adolf A., and Gardiner C. Means.
1932 *The Modern Corporation and Private Property.* New York: Commerce Clearing House.

Blair, John M.
1976 *The Control of Oil.* New York: Pantheon Books.

Blau, Peter M. and W. Richard Scott.
1962 *Formal Organizations.* San Francisco: Chandler.

Bliss, Michael.
1974 *A Living Profit.* Toronto: McClelland and Stewart.

1975 *Business Week,* May 26.

Campbell, Brian H.
1971 "Imperial Oil as a Corporate Entity". Unpublished paper.

Campbell, Robert W.
  1968 *The Economics of Soviet Oil and Gas*. Baltimore, Maryland: The Johns Hopkins Press.
  1976 *Trends in the Soviet Oil and Gas Industry*. Baltimore, Maryland: The Johns Hopkins Press.
  1976 *Canadian Business*. "The Top 200" (July).

Carlo, Antonio.
  1977 "The Oil Crisis and the Iron Law of Underdevelopment". *Telos*, 31: 5 – 34.

Chandler, Alfred D., Jr.
  1962 *Strategy and Structure*. Cambridge, Mass.: M.I.T. Press.

Cordell, Arthur J.
  1971 *The Multinational Firm, Foreign Direct Investment, and Canadian Science Policy*. Ottawa: Information Canada.

  1975 *Daedalus* (Fall). *The Oil Crisis: in Perspective*.

Dalton, Melville.
  1959 *Men Who Manage*. New York: John Wiley.

Davis, Edward M.
  1969 *Canada's Oil Industry*. Toronto: McGraw-Hill.

Debanné, J. G.
  1978 "Evolution of Canadian Oil Policy and Canadian – U.S. Energy Relations". Daniel Glenday, Hubert Guindon, and Allan Turowetz, eds. *Modernization and the Canadian State*. Toronto: Macmillan of Canada.

Deboice, Larry.
  1975 "Work Orientation as a Moderator of the Task Environment-Job Attitude Relationship." M.A. Thesis, University of Calgary.

Degré, Gérard.
  1941 "The Sociology of Knowledge and the Problem of Truth". *The Journal of the History of Ideas*, 2: 110 – 15.

Energy, Mines and Resources Canada.
  1976 *An Energy Strategy for Canada*. Ottawa: Supply and Services Canada.

Engler, Robert.
  1961 *The Politics of Oil*. Chicago: University of Chicago Press.
  1977 *The Brotherhood of Oil*. Chicago: University of Chicago Press.

  1976 *The Financial Post 300* (Summer).

1976 *The Financial Post Survey of Oils 1976*. Toronto: Maclean-Hunter.

1978 *The Financial Post*, February 25.

1979 *The Financial Post*, May 26.

Frank, Andre Gunder.

1967 *Capitalism and Underdevelopment in Latin America*. New York: Monthly Review Press.

Freeman, J.M.

1966 *Biggest Sellout in History*. Edmonton: Alberta NDP.

Galbraith, John Kenneth.

1971 *The New Industrial State*, 2nd ed. Boston: Houghton Mifflin.

Giddens, Anthony.

1976 *New Rules of Sociological Method*. New York: Basic Books.

Gasler, Barney G., and Anselm Strauss.

1967 *The Discovery of Grounded Theory*. Chicago: Aldine-Atherton.

Gonzalez, Arthuro.

1978 "Mexican Time Bomb". *Maclean's*, June 12: 24 – 38. Toronto: Maclean-Hunter.

Government of Canada.

1972 *Foreign Direct Investment in Canada* (The Gray Report). Ottawa: Information Canada.

Hanson, Eric J.

1958 *Dynamic Decade*. Toronto: McClelland and Stewart.

Harré, R.

1960 *An Introduction to the Logic of the Sciences*. London: Macmillan.

1972 *The Philosophies of Science*. London: Oxford University Press.

Hartshorn, J.E.

1962 *Oil Companies and Governments*. London: Faber and Faber.

Hedley, Max J.

1976 "Independent Commodity Production and the Dynamics of Tradition". *Canadian Review of Sociology and Anthropology*, 13: 413-21.

Helliwell, John.

1977 "Frontier Gas: Economic Indigestion". *Northern Perspectives*, 5: 1 – 4.

Hillborn, James D., ed.
1968 *Dusters and Gushers: The Canadian Oil Industry*. Toronto: Pitt Publishing.

Homans, George Casper.
1974 *Social Behavior: Its Elementary Forms*, rev. ed. New York: Harcourt, Brace, Jovanovich.

Hook, Sidney.
1962 *From Hegel to Marx*. Ann Arbor: University of Michigan Press.

Horton, John.
1964 "The Dehumanization of Alienation and Anomie". *British Journal of Sociology*, 15: 283 – 300.

House, J. Douglas.
1974 "Entrepreneurial Career Patterns of Residential Real Estate Agents in Montreal". *Canadian Review of Sociology and Anthropology*, 11: 110 – 24.

1975 "Durkheim and the Realist Philosophy of Science: Some New Lessons from an Old Master". *Sociological Analysis and Theory*, 5: 237 – 54.

1976 "A Note on Positivism". *The Insurgent Sociologist*, 6: 94 – 103.

1977a "The Social Organization of Multinational Corporations: Canadian Subsidiaries in the Oil Industry". *Canadian Review of Sociology and Anthropology*, 14: 1 – 14.

1977b *Contemporary Entrepreneurs*. Westport, Conn.: Greenwood Press.

1977c "In Defense of Karl Mannheim: The Sociology of Knowledge, Epistemology, and Methodology." *Sociological Analysis and Theory*, 7: 207 – 24.

1978 "Oil Companies in Aberdeen: The Strategy of Incorporation". *The Scottish Journal of Sociology*, 3: 85 – 102.

Keat, Russell, and John Urry.
1975 *Social Theory as Science*. London: Routledge and Kegan Paul.

Krohn, Roger G.
1974 "The Sociology of Knowledge and Science: Toward a Common Frame of Reference." Paper delivered at the 8th World Congress of Sociology, Toronto, Canada.

———, Berkeley Fleming, and Marilyn Manzer.
1977 *The Other Economy: The Internal Logic of Local Rental Housing*. Toronto: Peter Martin Associates.

Kuhn, Thomas.
　1962　*The Structure of Scientific Revolutions*. Chicago: University of Chicago Press.

Laxer, James.
　1970　*The Energy Poker Game*. Toronto: New Press.
　1974　*Canada's Energy Crisis*. Toronto: James Lewis and Samuel.
　――― and Anne Martin, eds.
　1976　*The Big Tough Expensive Job: Imperial Oil and the Canadian Economy*. Toronto: Press Porcepic.

Levitt, Kari.
　1970　*Silent Surrender*. Toronto: Macmillan of Canada.

　1978　*Maclean's*, July 10. Toronto: Maclean-Hunter.

Mannheim, Karl.
　1936　*Ideology and Utopia*. New York: Harcourt, Brace and World.

Marx, Karl.
　1887　*Das Kapital* (3 vols.). Moscow: Progress Publishers.

McLuhan, Marshall.
　1964　*Understanding Media*. New York: McGraw-Hill.

Mead, George H.
　1934　*Mind, Self, and Society*. Chicago: University of Chicago Press.

Merton, Robert K.
　1948　"The Bearing of Empirical Research Upon the Development of Social Theory". *American Sociological Review*, 13: 505 – 15.

Miller, Delbert C.
　1970　*Handbook of Research Design and Social Measurement*. 2nd ed. New York: David McKay.

Mills, C. Wright.
　1951　*White Collar*. New York: Oxford University Press.
　1956　*The Power Elite*. London: Oxford University Press.

　1973 – 74　Nickle's *Canadian Oil Register*. Calgary, Alberta: C. O. Nickle Publications.

O'Connor, H.
　1955　*The Empire of Oil*. New York: Monthly Review Press.
　1963　*World Crisis in Oil*. New York: Monthly Review Press.

Odell, Peter R.
  1970 *Oil and World Power: A Geographical Interpretation.* Harmondsworth, Middlesex: Penguin Books.

  1976 *Oilweek*, May 17. Calgary: Maclean-Hunter.
  1977 *Oilweek*, July 18. Calgary: Maclean-Hunter.
  1977 *Oilweek*, December 19. Calgary: Maclean-Hunter.
  1979 *Oilweek*, May 14. Calgary: Maclean-Hunter.
  1979 *Oilweek*, June 18. Calgary: Maclean-Hunter.

Patchen, Martin.
  1965 *Some Questionnaire Measures of Employee Motivation and Morale: A Report on Their Reliability and Validity.* Monograph No. 14. University of Michigan: Institute for Social Research.
  1970 *Participation, Achievement and Involvement on the Job.* Englewood Cliffs, N.J.: Prentice-Hall.

Penrose, Edith T.
  1968 *The Large International Firm in Developing Countries: The International Petroleum Industry.* London: George Allen and Unwin.

Polanyi, Karl.
  1957 *The Great Transformation.* Boston: Beacon Press.

Popper, Karl.
  1959 *The Logic of Scientific Discovery.* New York: Harper and Row.

Pratt, Larry.
  1976 *The Tar Sands: Syncrude and the Politics of Oil.* Edmonton: Hurtig.

Price, James L.
  1972 *Handbook of Organizational Measurement.* Lexington, Mass: D. C. Heath.

Riesman, David.
  1961 *The Lonely Crowd.* New Haven: Yale University Press.

Rudner, Richard S.
  1966 *Philosophy of Social Science.* Englewood Cliffs, N.J.: Prentice-Hall.

Ryan, Alan.
  1970 *The Philosophy of the Social Sciences.* London: Macmillan.

Safarian, A.E.
  1966 *Foreign Ownership of Canadian Industry*. Toronto: McGraw-Hill.

Sahlins, Marshall D.
  1965 "On the Sociology of Primitive Exchange". Michael Banton, ed. *The Relevance of Models in Social Anthropology*. A.S.U. Monographs. New York: Praeger.

Sampson, Anthony.
  1975 *The Seven Sisters*. New York: Viking Press.

Schumpeter, J.A.
  1951 *Essays on Economic Topics*. Edited by Richard V. Clemence. Port Washington, N.Y.: Kennikat.

Shepard, Jon M.
  1973 "Technology, Division of Labor, and Alienation". *Pacific Sociological Review*, 16: 61 – 88.

Stebbins, Robert A.
  1970 "Career: The Subjective Approach". *The Sociological Quarterly*, 11: 32 – 49.

Stobaugh, Robert B.
  1975 "The Oil Companies in the Crisis". *Daedalus*, 104: 179 – 202.

Toffler, Alvin.
  1970 *Future Shock*. New York: Bantam Books.

Tugendhat, Christopher.
  1971 *The Multinationals*. London: Eyre and Spottiswoode.
  _____ and Adrian Hamilton.
  1975 *Oil: The Biggest Business*. rev. ed. London: Eyre Methuen.

Vollmer, Howard M., and Donald L. Mills, eds.
  1966 *Professionalization*. Englewood Cliffs, N.J.: Prentice-Hall.

Weber, Max.
  1930 *The Protestant Ethic and the Spirit of Capitalism*. London: Unwin University Books.
  1947 *The Theory of Social and Economic Organization*. New York: Oxford University Press.

White, Harrison C.
  1970 *Chains of Opportunity*. Cambridge, Mass.: Harvard University s.

Whyte, William H., Jr.
  1956 *The Organization Man*. Garden City, N.Y.: Doubleday Anchor.
Wilkins, Mira.
  1975 "The Oil Companies in Perspective". *Daedalus*, 104: 159 – 78.
Willson, Bruce F.
  1977 "Natural Gas and Public Interest". *Canadian Forum*, 57: 5 – 8.

Zieber, George Henry.
  1971 "Inter- and Intra-City Location Patterns of Oil Offices for Calgary and Edmonton, 1950 – 1970". Ph.D. Dissertation, University of Alberta.